Essential Skills
for Reading Success

Strategies for Reading Comprehension and Test Taking

RALLY! ®
EDUCATION

We're all about student success! ®

Second Edition
New & Updated Content

Howard I. Berrent, Ph.D.

Edward R. Nasello

Acknowledgments

ISBN 978-1-4204-4916-7
R 4916-7

1209.MAQ

Printed on recycled paper. ♻

Executive Editor: Amy Collins
Project Manager: Edward Nasello
Design Director: Jean-Paul Vest
Illustrator: Donna Stackhouse

Photo Credits: p.21 ©123RF.com/Rosemary Buffoni; p.27 ©123RF.com/LaszloIlyes; p.30 ©123RF.com/Dave Wetzel;
p.44 ©123RF.com/Sebastian Kaulitzki; p.45 ©123RF.com/Sunaganov Dmitry; p.50 wikimedia/Paul Friel/snowmanradio, Dr. Gordon E.
Robertson, N.S. Fish and Wildlife Service/David Brnzinski/Dr. Thomas Barnes/Donna Dewhurst/, NOAA NESDIS,ORA/Michael Van
Woert/Mary Holllinger, William Lorenz; p.54 ©123RF.com/Andi Berger; p.62 ©123RF.com/Ivan Kmit; p.63 photo courtesy of the
Library of Congress; p.74-75 photos courtesy of the Library of Congress; p.81 photos courtesy of the Library of Congress;
p.84 ©123RF.com/Jose Manuel Gelpi Diaz; p.92 ©iStockphoto/Synergee; p.93 ©iStockphoto/sjlocke, ©123RF.com/Anneke Schram;
p.104 wikimedia/Michael Maggs. p.108 Ales Tosovsky; p.124 photo courtesy of OAR/National Undersea Research Program (NURP);
p.128 photo courtesy of OAR/NURP, M. Herko; p.138 ©123RF.com/Oleksandr Staroseltsev; p.139 ©iStockphoto/Vlingva;
p.151 photo courtesy of US Fish and Wildlife Service/Steve Maslowski

RALLY! EDUCATION
22 Railroad Avenue
Glen Head, NY 11545
1·888·99·RALLY
www.RALLYEDUCATION.com

Table of Contents

Introduction

Welcome to *Essential Skills for Reading Success: Strategies for Reading Comprehension and Test Taking*.

Being a successful reader means that you understand what you read. There are 14 key skills a reader needs to be a great reader. This book teaches these skills and strategies for how to use them.

The 14 Essential Skills for Reading Success are:

1 **Recall Facts and Details**
2 **Identify Main Idea**
3 **Identify Sequence**
4 **Analyze Language and Vocabulary**
5 **Analyze Character, Plot, and Setting**
6 **Recognize Cause and Effect**
7 **Compare and Contrast**
8 **Distinguish Fact from Opinion**
9 **Make Predictions**
10 **Draw Conclusions**
11 **Make Inferences**
12 **Analyze Point of View and Purpose**
13 **Identify Literary Forms and Sources of Information**
14 **Apply Prior Knowledge**

Throughout this book, you will read many different types of passages and answer different kinds of questions. *Strategies*, *Hints*, and *Reminders* are provided to make learning easier for you.

Essential Skills for Reading Success is divided into four parts:

Part A — Reading Skills One-by-One

Part B — Reading Skills Review

Part C — Reading Skills All Together

Part D — Assessments

Completing all of the lessons in this book will help you to master the 14 Essential Skills for Reading Success. You will be a better reader and a better test taker!

PART A:
Reading Skills One-by-One

In this section of the book, each of the 14 Essential Skills for Reading Success is taught in a separate lesson using Modeled Instruction, Guided Instruction, and Independent Practice. Part A also includes four Skill Review and four Vocabulary Review lessons to reinforce what you have learned in the individual skill lessons.

Modeled Instruction

There is a lot of information in a passage. When you answer questions about a passage, you must recall facts and details from the passage. You may even need to read some parts of the passage again to find the information you need to answer a question.

Even one sentence can have many facts and details.

The friendly firefighter rescued the cat that was in the tree.

Think about the facts and details that are in the sentence.

- The firefighter was friendly.
- The cat was in the tree.
- The firefighter rescued the cat.

Directions: Read the paragraph below and follow along to learn about recalling facts and details.

My great-grandmother, Anjuli Guha, was born in India. As a little girl, she lived on a farm where she helped tend cows and other animals. She also went to school in her village. It was convenient because her mother was the teacher. Great-grandmother often talks about the fun times she had as a child, though she was very happy when she moved to America.

STRATEGY: *Make a list of the important facts and details that you read in the paragraph.*

Complete the list below. Add another fact or detail from the paragraph that you think is important to remember.

Facts and Details About Anjuli Guha

1. She was born in India.

2. She helped tend cows on a farm.

3.

 Other details in the paragraph include: Anjuli Guha went to school in her village, her mother was a teacher, she had fun as a child, and she moved to America.

Directions: Read the paragraph below and follow along to answer a Facts and Details question.

> In many parts of the country, the leaves on trees change color in the fall. This change is due to the colder weather. The cold causes the leaves to lose their usual green color. As the green fades, colors such as orange and yellow appear on the leaves. A kind of sugar found in leaves makes many leaves turn red or purple. A forest in fall can be as colorful as a painting.

1 **Which colors are caused by sugar in leaves?**

Ⓐ green and orange

Ⓑ orange and yellow

Ⓒ yellow and red

Ⓓ red and purple

STRATEGY: *Look for key words that will help you find the answer to the question. The key words in this question are "colors" and "sugar."*

THINK Think about each answer choice and choose the best answer. Read the explanations below to check why each answer choice is wrong or right.

Ⓐ **green and orange**

Information in the paragraph tells you that leaves may change from green to orange. But there are no details that tell you this is caused by sugar. Choice A cannot be correct.

Ⓑ **orange and yellow**

The paragraph explains that leaves may become orange or yellow when it is cold. However, the paragraph does not tell you this has anything to do with sugar. Choice B cannot be correct.

Ⓒ **yellow and red**

The paragraph explains that leaves may turn yellow or red in cold weather. But only the change to red has something to do with sugar. Choice C cannot be correct.

Ⓓ **red and purple**

There is information in the paragraph that tells you sugar may cause leaves to turn red or purple. Choice D is the correct answer.

Guided Instruction

Directions: Read the passage below. Use *Before You Read*, *While You Read*, and *After You Read* strategies to help you answer questions about the passage.

BEFORE YOU READ:	• Look for clues that tell you what the passage will be about. • Look at the title and picture. Make predictions about the passage. • Look at the underlined words in the passage. Read the definitions for each of these words at the end of the passage.

WHILE YOU READ:	• Ask yourself questions while you read. • Look for information that you think is important. • Think about what the details in the passage tell you.

Now read this fictional passage. It is an example of realistic fiction.

Teresa's Plan

Teresa wanted to do something nice for her mother. She knew that her mother worked hard all week. Teresa went to the YMCA after school. Her mother picked Teresa up each day. Then she drove them home and made supper. She always had work to do after they ate. She might clean or wash clothes. Sometimes she worked at her desk.

Her mother always spent time with Teresa, too. Every night, she helped Teresa with homework. She read books with her. That was Teresa's favorite time of day. She loved to read with her mother. But her mother was often tired. She sometimes got sleepy while they were reading.

Teresa thought about what she could do herself. There were some things that she could not do. She was not allowed to use the stove. She couldn't drive to the store. She didn't have money to buy an <u>expensive</u> gift. But there were a lot of things a smart, eight-year-old girl could do. She could make a card. She could fix a special snack. She could help her mother do some <u>chores</u>.

At last Teresa had an idea she really liked. She waited until the weekend. On Saturday morning, she woke up early. The birds outside her window helped. They made a lot of noise. The sun was shining in, too. She went to the kitchen. She wanted to hurry. Her mother would be up soon.

She got a muffin from the breadbox. She put it on a pretty plate. Then, she got some grapes and put them on the plate, too. She saw some strawberries in the refrigerator. She found the biggest strawberry and put it on the plate. Then she poured some juice into a glass. Teresa put the food and a napkin on the tray. There was one more thing to do. She went outside and got a flower. She added that to the tray. Then she put a book under her arm.

Teresa's mother was very surprised to see Teresa by her bed. She sat up and smiled.

"What is all this?" she asked.

"I brought you breakfast in bed," Teresa told her. "Now you can eat and relax. I will read to you."

Teresa's mother took the tray. She patted the bed beside her. While Teresa read, her mother ate her muffin and fruit. She drank the juice. She smiled the whole time. Teresa finished reading. She looked at her mother. Her mother was still smiling.

"Do you know what I think?" her mother asked.

"What?" said Teresa.

"I think that I have the sweetest eight-year-old girl in the world."

Passage Vocabulary Words

chores – work that must be done

expensive – costs a lot of money

relax – to rest

AFTER YOU READ:
- Think about what you have just read.
- Read questions about the passage.
- Look for information in the passage that will help you answer the questions. You may want to make a list of facts and details.

Guided Instruction

Directions: Read questions 1–3. Next to each question is a hint that will help you answer each question. Choose the best answer to questions 1 and 2. Write your answer for question 3.

---

1   Teresa wants to do something nice for

Ⓐ   someone at the YMCA

Ⓑ   her mother

Ⓒ   herself

Ⓓ   a friend

HINT Use key words from the question to help you find the answer. The key words in this question are "do something nice." Look for these words in the passage. You should be able to find the information you need to answer the question.

---

2   What is something that Teresa could NOT do?

Ⓐ   make a card

Ⓑ   help with chores

Ⓒ   use the stove

Ⓓ   make a snack

HINT Use the key words "Teresa" and "could not" to find the part of the passage where the answer might be. Read this part of the passage again. Look for details you need to answer the question.

---

3   What did Teresa do while her mother ate her breakfast?

HINT Find the paragraph that tells about Teresa's mother eating breakfast. Read this paragraph again to find the details you need to answer the question.

_____

_____

_____

_____

Independent Practice

Directions: Answer the following questions on your own. For questions 4, 5, and 6, choose the correct answer. For question 7, you must write out your answer.

---

4 How does Teresa get home each day after school?

Ⓐ the YMCA bus

Ⓑ a school bus

Ⓒ she walks

Ⓓ her mother drives her

5 Why does Teresa want to do something nice for her mother?

Ⓐ Her mother works hard.

Ⓑ Her mother is sad.

Ⓒ Her mother asked her to.

Ⓓ She wants to use the stove.

---

6 What woke Teresa up on Saturday morning?

Ⓐ her mother

Ⓑ an alarm clock

Ⓒ the birds and the sun

Ⓓ the phone

---

7 What does Teresa put on the tray for her mother's breakfast?

_____

_____

_____

_____

Modeled Instruction

A main idea is what a passage, or part of a passage, is mostly about. To identify the main idea, you must think about all of the information you have read. You need to ask yourself, "What is this mostly about?" Some questions may ask about the main idea of a passage. Other questions may just ask about the main idea of a paragraph or sentence.

The details that you read will help you to identify the main idea.

Detail + Detail + Detail + Detail = Main Idea

Directions: Read the paragraph below and follow along to learn about main ideas.

> When they saw how rainy it was outside, the kids groaned. But they decided not to let the bad weather stop them. Matt got out his pencils and started drawing pictures. Erin practiced her violin. Amy practiced playing basketball using a trash can. James made paper airplanes that he sailed across the house. Kim painted her rocking chair.

STRATEGY: *Make a graphic organizer to help identify the main idea of the paragraph.*

Details from the paragraph are shown in the graphic organizer below. Write the main idea of the paragraph in the center circle.

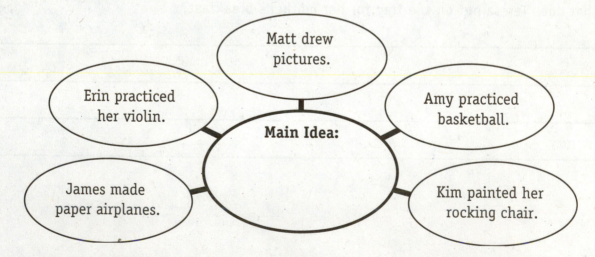

THINK All of the details in the graphic organizer explain how the kids spent their day. It seems like they had fun even though it was raining. Maybe this is the main idea of the paragraph.

Directions: Read the paragraph below and follow along to answer a Main Idea question.

> You may think clocks are a modern machine, but they have been around for a long time. Early clocks, called sundials, used sunlight and shadows to tell time. Later clocks used springs that you would wind up. These clocks showed the time using two or three "arms." The arms would move around a circle of numbers. The numbers that the arms pointed to would tell you what time it is. Today, many clocks are electric and have tiny lights to show numbers that tell you what time it is.

1 **This paragraph would most likely appear in a passage titled**

(A) "Modern Machines"

(B) "How Sundials Work"

(C) "The History of Clocks"

(D) "Wind-Up Clocks"

STRATEGY: *To think of the best title, you must know the main idea. You may want to make a graphic organizer or a list of details to help you identify the main idea. Then, think of a title that fits best with the main idea.*

THINK Think about each answer choice and choose the best answer. Read the explanations below to check why each answer choice is wrong or right.

(A) **"Modern Machines"**

This paragraph suggests that some clocks are modern machines. However, it also tells you about older clocks. Choice A cannot be correct.

(B) **"How Sundials Work"**

There is information in the paragraph about how sundials work. However, there is also information about other ways to tell time. This title does not describe what the paragraph is mostly about. Choice B cannot be correct.

(C) **"The History of Clocks"**

This paragraph has a lot of information about clocks from the past and today. The paragraph is mostly about the history of clocks. This title goes best with the main idea of the paragraph. Choice C is correct.

(D) **"Wind-Up Clocks"**

The paragraph does tell you about wind-up clocks. But there are also many details about other clocks. This title does not describe what the paragraph is mostly about. Choice D cannot be correct.

Identify Main Idea

Guided Instruction

Directions: Read the passage below. Use *Before You Read*, *While You Read*, and *After You Read* strategies to help you answer questions about the passage.

BEFORE YOU READ:	• Look for clues that tell you what the passage will be about. • Look at the pictures. Make predictions about the passage. • Look at the underlined words in the passage. Read the definitions for each of these words at the end of the passage.

WHILE YOU READ:	• Ask yourself questions while you read. • Look for information that you think is important. • Think about what the details in the passage tell you.

Now read this nonfiction passage. It is an example of a science essay.

Do you like bugs? You might like them, or you might not. But bugs are everywhere. Not all bugs are insects. But all insects are bugs. Ants, bees, and flies are insects. Spiders are not. How can you tell if you are looking at an insect?

What makes a bug an insect? All insects are alike in certain ways. They all breathe air. They all have six legs. They all have three body parts. There is the head at the front. The thorax is in the middle. And the abdomen is at the end.

Another thing that makes a bug an insect is its <u>skeleton</u>. An insect skeleton is not on the inside like yours is. It is around the outside of the insect's body. The skeleton protects the insect from getting hurt. It is strong, but it is light. And it is not as stiff as bone. This is so the insect can hop, walk, or fly.

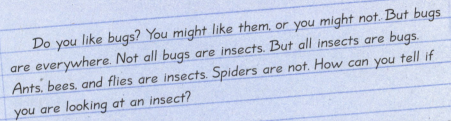

Insects can be <u>annoying</u>. But they are really amazing, too. And some of them are helpful to people. Some moths make silk, which we use for beautiful clothes. Ladybugs eat other insects that can hurt farmers' <u>crops</u>. Bees, of course, make the honey we love. Bees and other insects also spread <u>pollen</u> from plant to plant. This is important because some plants cannot grow unless they have pollen from other plants.

In a way, insects rule Earth. They were here long before the dinosaurs. They were the first animals to be able to fly. They live all over the world. They are on the ground, in the water, and in the sky. There are more insects than any other kind of animal—more than a million different kinds so far. And new kinds of insects are being discovered all the time.

The next time you see a creepy crawler, check it out. Now you will know if it is an insect!

Passage Vocabulary Words

annoying – to bother a person; make a person angry

crops – plants that farmers grow for food

pollen – dust-like powder that comes from flowers and helps make new flowers grow

skeleton – bones inside a body

AFTER YOU READ:
- Think about what you have just read.
- Read questions about the passage.
- Look for information in the passage that will help you answer the questions. You may want to make a graphic organizer.

Guided Instruction

Directions: Read questions 1–3. Next to each question is a hint that will help you answer each question. Choose the best answer to questions 1 and 2. Write your answer for question 3.

---

1 **What would be the best title for this essay?**

 Ⓐ "Animals Around the World"

 Ⓑ "How Bees Make Honey"

 Ⓒ "Ladybugs Are Insects, Too"

 Ⓓ "Interesting Insects"

 HINT A good title tells the reader the main idea of a passage. Think about all of the information you have read. Ask yourself, "What is the essay mostly about?"

---

2 **The third paragraph in the essay tells mostly about**

 Ⓐ how insects move

 Ⓑ the body parts of an insect

 Ⓒ the skeleton of an insect

 Ⓓ your skeleton

 HINT To answer this question, you only need to look at the third paragraph. Think about the important facts in this paragraph. What do most of these facts tell you about?

---

3 **What is the fourth paragraph mainly about? Explain which facts and details in the paragraph help you to know what the main idea is.**

 HINT Read the fourth paragraph. What are all the details describing? What are these facts and details telling you about? This is the main idea. Include this information in your answer.

_____

_____

_____

_____

Independent Practice

Directions: Answer the following questions on your own. For questions 4, 5, and 6, choose the correct answer. For question 7, you must write out your answer.

4 This essay is mostly about

Ⓐ where insects live

Ⓑ what insects are like

Ⓒ how many insects there are

Ⓓ how insects help people

5 What is the main idea of the second paragraph?

Ⓐ how insects breathe

Ⓑ where an insect's head is

Ⓒ ways that all insects are alike

Ⓓ insects' legs

6 Which fact below would fit best in the second paragraph of the essay?

Ⓐ The mayfly lives for just a few hours.

Ⓑ Some insects have tricks to scare away enemies.

Ⓒ There are more beetles than any other kind of insect.

Ⓓ Most insects hatch from eggs.

7 What would make a good title for the fifth paragraph? Explain why you think this would make a good title.

_____

_____

_____

_____

Modeled Instruction

Sequence is the order in which things happen. Actions or events in a passage can be put in order from first to last.

Sometimes things appear in the passage in the order that they happen.

<u>Kristina put on her jacket</u> before <u>she went outside</u>.
     FIRST   **SECOND**

Sometimes things do not appear in the passage in the order that they happen.

<u>Kristina went outside</u> after <u>she put on her jacket</u>.
  SECOND   **FIRST**

Directions: Read the paragraph below and follow along to learn about sequence.

> Jana was in class getting ready for a big math test. Just when she thought she was prepared, she realized her pencil was missing. Right away, she thought that the boy next to her, Jeremy, had taken it. Jana thought he was playing a mean trick on her, and she felt angry. Then the teacher walked by and pointed to the floor. "Looks like you dropped your pencil, Jana," she said. Jana looked down and discovered her pencil was right under her desk.

STRATEGY: *Make a graphic organizer to show the order in which things happen.*

Complete the graphic organizer below. Look at the details in the first and second boxes. What detail do you think belongs in the third box?

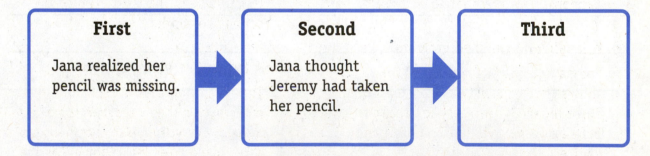

First	Second	Third
Jana realized her pencil was missing.	Jana thought Jeremy had taken her pencil.	

THINK After Jana thought Jeremy had taken her pencil, she found out her pencil had fallen onto the floor. This is the third thing that happened.

Directions: Read the paragraph below and follow along to answer a Sequence question.

> Ladybugs may be small, but they spend a lot of time growing. Ladybugs start out as eggs. These eggs break open after about a week. The ladybug baby, or "larva," comes out of the egg. This larva has a black shell on it. Later, the ladybug will grow too big for the shell, which will fall off. The ladybug keeps growing new shells until the bug is all grown up. Then, the pretty red bug flies away.

1 Which of the following happens first?

Ⓐ A ladybug loses its shell.

Ⓑ A ladybug is finished growing.

Ⓒ A ladybug flies away.

Ⓓ A ladybug is inside an egg.

STRATEGY: *You may want to make a graphic organizer to help answer this question. Another strategy you may use is to make a list. You can list the things that happened in the order that they happened.*

THINK Think about each answer choice and choose the best answer. Read the explanations below to check why each answer choice is wrong or right.

Ⓐ **A ladybug loses its shell.**

The paragraph explains that a ladybug loses its shell after it is a baby, or larva. This is not the first thing that happens. Choice A cannot be correct.

Ⓒ **A ladybug flies away.**

The last part of the paragraph tells you that a ladybug is ready to fly away when it is all grown up. This is the last thing that happens. Choice C cannot be correct.

Ⓑ **A ladybug is finished growing.**

The paragraph tells you about the things that happen as a ladybug grows. There are many things that happen before a ladybug is finished growing. Choice B cannot be correct.

Ⓓ **A ladybug is inside an egg.**

The first thing that is explained in the paragraph is that a ladybug is inside an egg. Everything else that happens takes place after this. Choice D is the correct answer.

Guided Instruction

Directions: Read the passage below. Use *Before You Read*, *While You Read*, and *After You Read* strategies to help you answer questions about the passage.

BEFORE YOU READ:	• Look for clues that tell you what the passage will be about. • Look at the title and picture. Make predictions about the passage. • Look at the underlined words in the passage. Read the definitions for each of these words at the end of the passage.
WHILE YOU READ:	• Ask yourself questions while you read. • Look for information that you think is important. • Think about what the details in the passage tell you.

Now read this passage. The first part tells a story. The second part includes examples of functional text. It includes lists, directions, and instructions.

Keesha's Lists

Keesha's grandmother was not feeling well, and Keesha and her mom were going to take some chicken soup to her. It was going to be a busy day, so Keesha decided to make a list. Her mother said that making a list was a good way to get <u>organized</u>. Keesha got a pen and a piece of paper. She wrote what they needed to do. Then Keesha's mother told her what they needed to buy at the store. Keesha wrote that down, too. Keesha asked her mother how they would make the chicken soup. As her mother told her, Keesha wrote the <u>instructions</u>. Then, Keesha wrote down the directions to Grandma's house, just for fun.

Keesha's To Do List

Bring soup to Grandma

Make chicken soup

Get <u>groceries</u>

Grocery List

3 chicken breasts, with bones and skin

1 onion

3 carrots

3 sticks of celery

1 bunch of parsley

1 box of egg noodles

Directions to Grandma's

- Take Maple Avenue to Pine Street.
- At the corner of Maple and Pine, make a left onto Pine.
- Continue to the corner of Pine and Birch.
- Make a right turn onto Birch.
- Grandma's house is number 32. It is the third house on the left-hand side of Birch Street.

P.S. Be careful not to spill the soup!

Recipe for Chicken Soup

1. Fill a large pot with water.
   While it is heating, cut up the carrots, celery, and onion. Chop 1/2 cup of parsley.
2. When the water is <u>boiling</u>, put the chicken and half of the onion in the pot.
3. Boil the chicken and onion until the chicken is cooked.
4. Take the chicken from the water, and remove the meat from the bones.
5. Cut the chicken into bite-sized pieces and put it back into the water.
6. Add the celery and carrots, the rest of the onion, parsley, salt, and pepper.
7. Simmer until the vegetables are <u>tender</u>.
8. Bring the soup back to a boil, and add the uncooked egg noodles.
9. Cook the noodles as directed on the noodle package. When the noodles are done, so is the soup!

Passage Vocabulary Words

boiling – so hot that it begins to bubble

groceries – food you buy at the store

instructions – steps that tell how to do something

organized – having a plan for doing something

tender – soft

AFTER YOU READ:
- Think about what you have just read.
- Read questions about the passage.
- Look for information in the passage that will help you answer the questions. You may want to make a graphic organizer.

Guided Instruction

Directions: Read questions 1–3. Next to each question is a hint that will help you answer each question. Choose the best answer to questions 1 and 2. Write your answer for question 3.

---

1 **What does the soup recipe say you should do after you remove the chicken from the bones, but before you put it back in the water?**

  Ⓐ Add the rest of the onion.

  Ⓑ Add the egg noodles.

  Ⓒ Boil the chicken until cooked.

  Ⓓ Cut the meat into bite-sized pieces.

HINT To answer this question, you must put things in the order that they happen. Read the recipe again. Make a timeline to list things in the order they should be done.

First _____

_____

_____

_____

_____

_____

Last _____

---

2 **Which of the following happens first?**

  Ⓐ Keesha makes a list of the things they have to do.

  Ⓑ Keesha and her mother take soup to her grandmother.

  Ⓒ Keesha and her mother go to the store.

  Ⓓ Keesha and her mother make soup.

HINT Look at the information in the passage that tells what Keesha did. List these actions and events in the order that they happened. Ask yourself which happened first.

---

3 **List three things Keesha and her mother did before they went to see Grandma.**

HINT List the things Keesha and her mother did in the order that they did them. Identify three things they did before they went to see Grandma.

_____

_____

_____

_____

Independent Practice

Directions: Answer the following questions on your own. For questions 4, 5, and 6, choose the correct answer. For question 7, you must write out your answer.

---

4   Look at the boxes below.

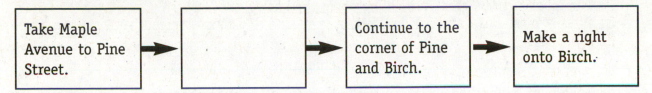

| Take Maple Avenue to Pine Street. | → | | → | Continue to the corner of Pine and Birch. | → | Make a right onto Birch. |

Which of the following should be placed in the empty box to complete the directions?

Ⓐ   Grandma's house is number 32.

Ⓑ   Continue to the corner of Pine and Birch.

Ⓒ   At the corner of Maple and Pine, make a left onto Pine.

Ⓓ   Go to the third house on the left-hand side of Birch Street.

---

5   When should you add carrots to the soup?

Ⓐ   when you put in the bite-sized meat and add the vegetables

Ⓑ   after the egg noodles and chicken are completely cooked

Ⓒ   after you simmer the vegetables

Ⓓ   when you are heating the water

6   What happened just before Keesha wrote her lists?

Ⓐ   Her mother told her what they needed to buy.

Ⓑ   They went to her grandmother's house.

Ⓒ   Her mother told her how to make the soup.

Ⓓ   She got a pen and a piece of paper.

---

7   Keesha's list of things to do is out of order. List the things she must do in the order that she should do them.

_____

_____

_____

_____

Modeled Instruction

Sometimes when you read you see new words or phrases. You may not know what they mean. You must look for clues to help you understand the meaning of these words and phrases.

If you read a sentence with a new word you do not know, look at the other words around it. You may find clues that help you understand what the new word means.

The *toboggan* was great for <u>sliding down the snowy hill</u>.

↑   ↑

new word   **clue**

In this sentence, "sliding down the snowy hill" tells you that a toboggan is a kind of sled used in snow.

Directions: Read the paragraph below and follow along to learn about analyzing language and vocabulary.

> When we visited Madison Mountain, we were amazed. It was so beautiful we did not want to leave. We wanted to <u>bring the experience home with us</u>. We wanted <u>something to help us remember it</u>. My friend Jules said we should each take a small rock as a *souvenir*. The rocks would always <u>remind us of what we did that special day</u>.

STRATEGY: *When you do not know the meaning of a word, look for clues in the paragraph to help you understand what the word means.*

Clues that can help you understand the meaning of the word *souvenir* have been underlined. Two of the clues are explained in the chart below. Add the last clue to the chart and explain what it tells you. What do you think the word *souvenir* means?

Clues	What does each clue tell you?
bring the experience home with us	A souvenir can be taken home.
something to help us remember it	A souvenir can help a person remember something.

THINK The phrase "remind us of what we did that special day" suggests that a souvenir is something that helps people remember special times. If you look at all the clues, this answer makes sense.

Directions: Read the paragraph below and follow along to answer a Language and Vocabulary question.

> Andre had been working hard all week. He was part of a group that was building a house for people who had no place to live. Andre kept thinking about what a good cause that was. At the end of the week, he did not get paid. Nobody did, and nobody wanted any money for his or her work. Andre and the other *volunteers* were pleased enough to have done a good thing.

1 What does the word *volunteers* mean?

Ⓐ people who have no homes

Ⓑ people who do work for no money

Ⓒ people who know about houses

Ⓓ people who cannot build things

STRATEGY: *You may want to make a chart to list clues that can help you to understand what the word* volunteers *means.*

THINK Think about each answer choice and choose the best answer. Read the explanations below to check why each answer choice is wrong or right.

Ⓐ **people who have no homes**

There are details in the paragraph about people without homes. However, the volunteers seem to be a different group of people. They are the ones who are building a house. Choice A cannot be correct.

Ⓑ **people who do work for no money**

Clues such as "working hard," "a good cause," and "did not get paid" suggest that volunteers are people who work without getting paid. They do this type of work to help others. Choice B is the correct answer.

Ⓒ **people who know about houses**

Part of the paragraph does explain that the volunteers are building a house. However, the word *volunteers* appears in a different part of the paragraph. The clues in the paragraph suggest that being a volunteer means something else. Choice C cannot be correct.

Ⓓ **people who cannot build things**

You can tell this is not the correct answer because the volunteers are building a house. This means they are able to build things. Choice D cannot be correct.

Guided Instruction

Directions: Read the passage below. Use *Before You Read*, *While You Read*, and *After You Read* strategies to help you answer questions about the passage.

BEFORE YOU READ:	• Look for clues that tell you what the passage will be about. • Look at the title and pictures. Make predictions about the passage. • Look at the underlined words in the passage. Read the definitions for each of these words at the end of the passage.

WHILE YOU READ:	• Ask yourself questions while you read. • Look for information that you think is important. • Think about what the details in the passage tell you.

Now read this fictional passage. It is an example of a poem.

Mr. Nobody

Anonymous

1   I know a funny little man,

2   As quiet as a mouse,

3   Who does the *mischief* that is done

4   In everybody's house!

5   *There's no one ever sees his face*,

6   And yet we all agree

7   That every plate we break was cracked

8   By Mr. Nobody.

9   'Tis he who always *tears* our books,

10 Who leaves the door *ajar*,

11 *He pulls the buttons from our shirts*,

12 And scatters pins afar;

13 That squeaking door will always squeak,

14 For, Friend, don't you see,

15 We leave the oiling to be done

16 By Mr. Nobody.

17 He puts damp wood upon the fire,

18 *That kettles cannot boil;*

19 His are the feet that bring in the mud,

20 And all the carpets soil.

21 The papers always are <u>mislaid</u>,

22 Who had them last but he?

23 There's not one tosses them about

24 But Mr. Nobody.

25 The finger marks upon the door

26 By none of us are made;

27 We never leave the **blinds** unclosed,

28 to let the curtains fade;

29 The ink we never spill; the boots

30 That lying around you see

31 Are not our boots; they all belong

32 To Mr. Nobody!

Passage Vocabulary Words

afar – far away

mislaid – lost

scatters – to spread around

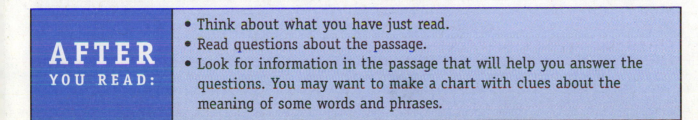

AFTER YOU READ:
- Think about what you have just read.
- Read questions about the passage.
- Look for information in the passage that will help you answer the questions. You may want to make a chart with clues about the meaning of some words and phrases.

Analyze Language and Vocabulary

Guided Instruction

Directions: Read questions 1–3. Next to each question is a hint that will help you answer each question. Choose the best answer to questions 1 and 2. Write your answer for question 3.

---

1 In line 10, the word *ajar* means

Ⓐ clean

Ⓑ closed

Ⓒ open

Ⓓ locked

HINT Thinking about how a word is used in a sentence can help you to understand the meaning of the word. Other words in the sentence might give you clues about its meaning. You may need to look at a few sentences to discover the meaning of a word.

---

2 The phrase *there's no one ever sees his face* suggests

Ⓐ Mr. Nobody doesn't have a face

Ⓑ Mr. Nobody is afraid of people

Ⓒ Mr. Nobody is not a real person

Ⓓ Mr. Nobody wears a mask over his face

HINT Compare the words in each answer choice with the words in the question. Which answer choice has the same meaning as the words in the question?

---

3 What do you think the phrase *he pulls the buttons from our shirts* means?

HINT Read the part of the poem where this phrase is used. What do the details tell you about what is happening? Who is this phrase telling you about?

_____

_____

_____

_____

Independent Practice

Directions: Answer the following questions on your own. For questions 4, 5, and 6, choose the correct answer. For question 7, you must write out your answer.

4 **The word *mischief* means**

Ⓐ mean behavior

Ⓑ naughty behavior

Ⓒ sad behavior

Ⓓ helpful behavior

5 **Read the different meanings for the word *tears*.**

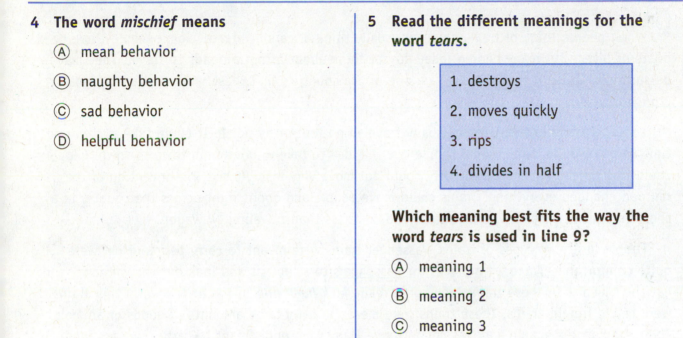

1. destroys

2. moves quickly

3. rips

4. divides in half

Which meaning best fits the way the word *tears* is used in line 9?

Ⓐ meaning 1

Ⓑ meaning 2

Ⓒ meaning 3

Ⓓ meaning 4

6 **Which words help the reader know what *blinds* are?**

Ⓐ *curtains* and *fade*

Ⓑ *never* and *leave*

Ⓒ *none* and *us*

Ⓓ *ink* and *spill*

7 **In line 18, what is the author trying to tell you by using the phrase *that kettles cannot boil*?**

_____

_____

_____

_____

Directions: Read the passage below and answer questions 1–7.

The Story of Railroads

When people think of traveling, they usually think of cars or planes. Some people think of boats or bikes. But many people today do not think about using railroads to travel. They may be surprised to learn that railroads are one of the country's first, best, and most used kinds of *transportation*.

Long before railroads, people usually traveled on foot or by horse. It could take a very long time to get around. Later, some people got the idea to take wagons from town to town. People could ride on these wagons, but they could not move very fast. At last, the invention of the railroad changed everything. Trains could move people and goods right across the country in a short amount of time. It was also safer and cost less than traveling by wagon.

People built two types of trains. Passenger trains were meant to carry people. Most were quite comfortable. There were places for <u>passengers</u> to sleep, sit and look out the windows, and eat their meals. In these trains, you could really *kick back and put your feet up*. Other trains were called <u>freight</u> trains. These trains were meant to carry large amounts of goods or animals. These trains were simple and less comfortable. Many were only meant to carry cows or pigs.

The first trains were made in the early 1800s. These early trains were made in England. Later, other countries found out about them and built their own. These first trains were run by <u>steam</u> engines. These engines used fire to turn water into steam. The steam would then make the train's wheels turn. Steam trains did not work as well as today's engines. They worked well enough, though.

Many people loved riding trains. Trains allowed people to move around the country and live in many different places. Trains played a huge part in allowing America to grow. Although more people today drive cars than ride trains, trains are still important. Trains are even traveling all around the world as you read this!

Passage Vocabulary Words

freight – goods carried usually by trucks or trains

passengers – people who ride trains, cars, boats, buses, or airplanes

steam – gas made by heating water

Facts & Details, Main Idea, Sequence, Language & Vocabulary

Identify Main Idea

1 **What is the main idea of the third paragraph?**

- (A) Freight trains are made to carry many people.
- (B) Trains only carry animals such as pigs and cows.
- (C) All trains are very comfortable for people to ride in.
- ● Passenger trains and freight trains have different uses.

REM!NDER

This question asks you to find the main idea of one part of the passage. Read this part of the passage again and think about what it is mostly about.

Analyze Language and Vocabulary

2 **What does the word *transportation* mean?**

- (A) strong engines
- ● moving people or goods
- (C) comfortable place
- (D) inventing new machines

This question asks about the meaning of one word in the passage. Look in the passage for clues that help you to know what this word means.

Analyze Language and Vocabulary

3 Read the following sentence from the passage.

"In these trains, you could really *kick back and put your feet up*."

In this sentence, what does the author mean by *kick back and put your feet up*?

- (A) travel by walking
- (B) travel with animals
- ● feel very comfortable
- (D) dance and jump around

This question asks you to tell the meaning of a group of words in the passage. Think about how these words are used. Look for clues in the part of the passage where you find this sentence.

Recall Facts and Details

4 Which of the following is NOT used on a steam engine train?

- (A) wagons
- (B) fire
- (C) wheels
- (D) water

REM!NDER

The answer to this question can be found right in the passage. If you cannot remember what you have read, look for key words to help you find the answer in the passage.

Identify Main Idea

5 What is the main idea of this passage?

- (A) Railroads are not the best way to travel.
- (B) Railroads are an old and important invention.
- (C) New engines are better than steam engines.
- (D) Everyone likes to ride on trains.

REM!NDER

This question asks you to tell the main idea. The main idea is what the passage is mostly about.

Recall Facts and Details

6 Where were the first trains made?

 To answer this question, you need to recall facts and details from the passage. Look for key words in the passage that will help you find facts and details you can use to answer this question.

_____

_____

_____

_____

Identify Sequence

7 **Fill in the boxes below to show how the way people traveled changed over time. List the things people did to travel in the order that they did them.**

 To answer a question about sequence, you must list the things that happened in the order that they happened.

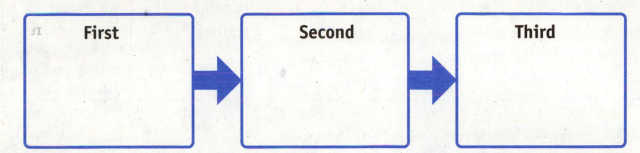

| First | Second | Third |

VOCABULARY REVIEW: Skills 1–4

Directions: Listed below are some words that were used in each of the passages you just read. Choose the correct words to complete the sentences on this page. You may look back at the passages to find the meaning of each word.

Teresa's Plan	Essay (no title)	Keesha's Lists	Mr. Nobody	The Story of Railroads
chores	annoying	boiling	afar	freight
expensive	crops	groceries	mislaid	passengers
relax	pollen	instructions	scatters	steam
	skeleton	organized		
		tender		

1 The sound of the car honking its horn was coming from _____, but it was still so loud that it quickly became _____ to us.

2 Raul became very tired from doing all of his _____. He needed some time to _____ before doing his homework.

3 My little sister always _____ all of her toys on the floor.

4 The scientist _____ the bones to make a _____ of a dinosaur.

5 Mr. O'Reilly grew many _____ on his farm.

6 Mrs. Cruz began _____ some vegetables on the stove. She also cooked a turkey until it was very _____.

7 The heavy boxes of _____ were placed on the truck to be delivered.

8 When the water was heated, it quickly turned into _____.

9 Eva went to the store to buy some _____. Some of the things she needed to buy were so _____ that she did not have enough money to buy them.

Directions: Some words you have already read in this book are used in the questions on this page. Use what you have learned about these words to help you answer questions 1–4.

1 Read the sentence below.

"The *passengers* on the bus were eager to begin their trip."

The word *passengers* means

(A) bus drivers

(B) guests

(C) people who travel

(D) neighbors

2 In which sentence is the word *mislaid* used correctly?

(A) My mother had mislaid her keys and could not find them.

(B) I was very tired because I had mislaid on the bed.

(C) Mr. Chang mislaid seeds on the ground to grow flowers.

(D) All of the books were neatly mislaid on the shelf.

3 Read the sentence below.

"Roberto followed the *instructions* to make a model airplane."

The word *instructions* means

(A) directions

(B) clues

(C) teachers

(D) rules

4 In which sentence is the word *pollen* used correctly?

(A) Larry poured some pollen over the grass.

(B) The pollen from the flowers made me sneeze.

(C) Clara filled her pockets with pollen.

(D) The pollen in the sand was very soft.

Vocabulary Challenge

Directions: Choose any three vocabulary review words from the top of page 34. Write sentences using each of these words.

1 _____

2 _____

3 _____

SKILL 5: Analyze Character, Plot, and Setting

Modeled Instruction

Most stories that you read will have at least one character, a plot, and a setting. A character is *who* the story is about. The plot is *what* the story is about. And the setting is *where* and *when* the story takes place.

When you read a story, ask yourself—

> Who is the story about?
> What is the story about?
> Where does the story take place?
> When does the story take place?

Directions: Read the paragraph below and follow along to learn about character, plot, and setting.

> On Tuesday morning, Evan was sitting in science class. Mr. Rumbolt, the teacher, was talking all about animals. Evan looked out the window. He noticed some birds building a nest in a nearby tree. Evan saw one bird gathering bits of straw to add to the nest. Suddenly, Mr. Rumbolt asked Evan a question. Evan had to admit he had not been listening to the lesson. Mr. Rumbolt said Evan had to pay attention—but added that watching animals, as Evan was doing, was a good way to learn about them.

STRATEGY: *Make a graphic organizer to help identify the characters, plot, and setting.*

Complete the graphic organizer below. Fill in the empty box to tell who the characters are in the paragraph you just read.

Who (Characters)	**What** (Plot)
	A boy was watching a bird outside. The boy was not paying attention in class.
Where (Setting)	**When** (Setting)
inside a classroom	on Tuesday morning during science class

THINK The characters are who a story is about. The paragraph on this page tells you about Evan and Mr. Rumbolt.

Directions: Read the paragraph below and follow along to answer a Setting question.

> Tommy sat on the edge of his seat and looked down at the court. The players were running quickly from side to side. Many people were cheering excitedly. Suddenly, one of the players passed the ball, and another caught it. Just as the time ran out, the player threw the ball into the basket and scored. Everyone in the stands began to holler and dance happily. Tommy had a great night, and he talked about it all week.

1 Where was Tommy?

Ⓐ at a basketball game

Ⓑ at the beach

Ⓒ at the library

Ⓓ at a shopping mall

STRATEGY: *Look in the paragraph for clues about the setting. List all of details that tell you about where Tommy was.*

THINK Think about each answer choice and choose the best answer. Read the explanations below to check why each answer choice is wrong or right.

Ⓐ **at a basketball game**

Details in the paragraph tell you that Tommy is near a court full of players who are passing and throwing a ball. He sees one player throw a ball into a basket. These clues suggest he is at a basketball game. Choice A is the correct answer.

Ⓒ **at the library**

There are seats at a library, and Tommy is sitting in a seat. However, details in the paragraph tell you that people are cheering. This would probably not happen at a library. Choice C cannot be correct.

Ⓑ **at the beach**

If Tommy were at the beach you would expect there to be sand and water. There are no details in the paragraph that suggest Tommy is at the beach. Choice B cannot be correct.

Ⓓ **at a shopping mall**

Details in the paragraph suggest that Tommy is in a busy place with many people. However, the people are not shopping. They are watching a game. Choice D cannot be correct.

Guided Instruction

Directions: Read the passage below. Use *Before You Read*, *While You Read*, and *After You Read* strategies to help you answer questions about the passage.

BEFORE YOU READ:	• Look for clues that tell you what the passage will be about. • Look at the title and picture. Make predictions about the passage. • Look at the underlined words in the passage. Read the definitions for each of these words at the end of the passage.

WHILE YOU READ:	• Ask yourself questions while you read. • Look for information that you think is important. • Think about what the details in the passage tell you.

Now read this fictional passage. It is an example of realistic fiction.

Afloat in a Boat

"I'm bored," said Tina to Tory, who was stretched out on the bed in their room.

Tory had finished one book and was reading another one. Tina liked to read, but not if there were more exciting things to do at their summer house by the lake.

"What do you want to do?" asked Tory, pulling on one of her pigtails.

Tina didn't have time for pigtails. She hardly had time to brush her hair. The twins weren't hard to tell apart. Tina's clothes were <u>mismatched</u> and wrinkled. Tory's were just the opposite.

"Let's ask Mom," said Tina. "She's usually got some ideas."

The girls went into the front room. Their mother was asleep, with a book in her lap, so the twins went to find their father. When they looked in back of the house, they noticed that the car was gone.

"Let's go down and feel the water," said Tina, pulling on Tory's arm.

"We're not supposed to swim alone," Tory reminded Tina, pulling back.

"We won't swim, silly, we're just going to feel the water."

The girls sat on the dock and <u>dangled</u> their feet in the water. Tiny fishes swam by their toes.

"I'm still bored," sighed Tina. "Let's get in the boat."

"I don't think we should, Tina. It's not a good idea."

"We'll just sit in it and float a little."

The girls stepped into the little rowboat. Tina untied the rope, and they each took an <u>oar</u>. They sat on the warm bottom of the boat and talked. The warm sun and lapping water were relaxing.

After a little while, they sat up and looked around.

"Look how far we floated!" gasped Tina.

"Where's your oar?" asked Tory.

Tina looked around. Several yards away, her oar was floating on the water. "It must have fallen out."

Tory tried to paddle with her oar, but the boat just went in circles. Tina looked pale. Tory's throat felt tight. A cool breeze made the girls shiver.

Then Tina pointed toward the house. Their mother was putting the <u>canoe</u> in the water. She began to paddle toward them. Paddling first on one side and then on the other, she moved in a straight line through the water.

"Sit still!" their mother called. "I'll be right there." After a few minutes, she was next to them. Frowning, she asked if they were all right. The girls nodded. She tied the rowboat to the canoe, picked up the floating oar, and began paddling back. The girls looked at each other, wondering what would happen next.

When they got to shore, the girls hopped out, happy to be back on land.

Their mother came over to them and said, "I wish when one of you had a bad idea, the other one would talk her out of it."

Tina glanced at Tory.

"No swimming for the rest of the day," their mother continued. "You could have drowned, or drifted so far that I wouldn't have seen you!"

"We're sorry, Mom," the girls <u>apologized</u>.

Just then, their father joined them. "I saw the whole thing," he said. "That was a dangerous thing to do. When you are allowed in the water again, you'll do something besides swim."

"What's that?" asked Tina.

"You'll learn how to row a boat."

Passage Vocabulary Words

apologized – to tell someone you are sorry
           for doing something wrong

canoe – a type of small boat

dangled – to hang down

mismatched – not matching properly

oar – a piece of wood with one flat end, used
       to paddle a boat through the water

AFTER
YOU READ:

- Think about what you have just read.
- Read questions about the passage.
- Look for information in the passage that will help you answer the questions. You may want to make a graphic organizer.

Analyze Character, Plot, and Setting

Guided Instruction

Directions: Read questions 1–3. Next to each question is a hint that will help you answer each question. Choose the best answer to questions 1 and 2. Write your answer for question 3.

---

1 Where does most of the story take place?

   Ⓐ in the girls' bedroom

   Ⓑ in the front room

   Ⓒ on the lake

   Ⓓ in back of the house

 HINT Use a story map to organize important information about the story. A story map shows what happens (plot), who does what (character), and where or when the events take place (setting). This question is about the setting.

---

2 What can you tell about Tina from reading the passage?

   Ⓐ She does not like adventures.

   Ⓑ She does not like the summer house.

   Ⓒ She likes having a twin.

   Ⓓ She would rather be active.

HINT This question asks about a character in the story. The things that a character does or says can tell you a lot about that person. Think about Tina's actions in the passage.

---

3 What is this passage about? Explain the plot of the story.

 HINT To summarize the plot of a passage, you only need to include the most important details. Think about what information would be important to know.

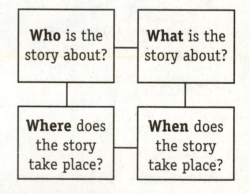

Who is the story about?	**What** is the story about?
Where does the story take place?	**When** does the story take place?

_____

_____

_____

_____

Independent Practice

Directions: Answer the following questions on your own. For questions 4, 5, and 6, choose the correct answer. For question 7, you must write out your answer.

4 Tory can best be described as

Ⓐ careful

Ⓑ silly

Ⓒ wild

Ⓓ rude

5 Where is the girls' mother when the story begins?

Ⓐ in her bedroom

Ⓑ in the canoe

Ⓒ in the front room

Ⓓ in the car

6 Which two characters in the story seem the most alike?

Ⓐ Tory and her mother

Ⓑ Tina and her father

Ⓒ Tory and Tina

Ⓓ Tina and her mother

7 How would you describe Tina? Support your answer with at least one detail from the story.

_____

_____

_____

SKILL 6: Recognize Cause and Effect

Modeled Instruction

There are many details in a passage. Sometimes the details are connected to each other—they have a cause-and-effect relationship. A cause answers the question "Why did it happen?" An effect answers the question "What happened?"

CAUSE — The dog began barking.

EFFECT — The frightened cat ran away.

Directions: Read the paragraph below and follow along to learn about cause and effect.

> Angelica knew that some people use computers every day. She never became interested in computers, though. Her family did not have one. Angelica really did not know how computers worked. Then, one day she went to the library and saw a long row of computers. People were using them to do many different things. Some searched for books and others checked messages. The next day, Angelica learned that her school had a computer room. There, students could learn how to use computers. Now, for the first time, Angelica felt curious about computers.

STRATEGY: *Make a graphic organizer to show causes and effects that are connected to each other.*

The paragraph you just read explains that Angelica became curious about computers. There are a few reasons why this happened. The graphic organizer below shows one reason. See if you can find another reason. Fill in the empty box.

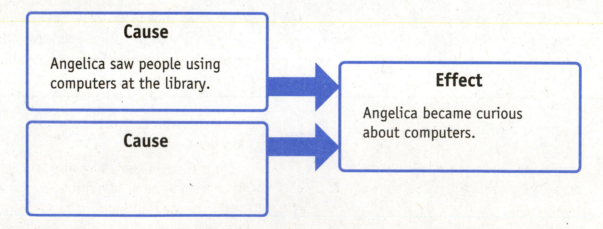

Cause

Angelica saw people using computers at the library.

Cause

Effect

Angelica became curious about computers.

THINK Details in the paragraph explain that Angelica learned her school had a computer room that students could use. This probably made her more curious about computers.

Directions: Read the paragraph below and follow along to answer a Cause and Effect question.

> One of the most interesting types of fish is the salmon. Salmon live in the salty water of the ocean. However, baby salmon cannot live in salt water. When salmon are going to have babies, they must swim into fresh water. Some salmon swim many miles from the ocean into rivers and streams. Often, these fish have to swim up powerful rivers. Once in the fresh water, the salmon may safely lay their eggs. Then, it's time to return to the ocean.

1   Because baby salmon cannot live in salt water

Ⓐ salmon live in the ocean

Ⓑ salmon have to stay in rivers

Ⓒ salmon usually stay in salt water

Ⓓ salmon swim to fresh water to lay eggs

STRATEGY: *This question tells you the cause. You must find the effect. Look for details in the paragraph that help you connect the cause and the effect.*

THINK   Think about each answer choice and choose the best answer. Read the explanations below to check why each answer choice is wrong or right.

Ⓐ **salmon live in the ocean**

The paragraph explains that the ocean water is salty. Baby salmon cannot live in salt water. There is no cause-and-effect relationship. Choice A cannot be correct.

Ⓑ **salmon have to stay in rivers**

It is true that salmon may have to swim up rivers. But they do not have to stay there. They can return to the ocean. Choice B cannot be correct.

Ⓒ **salmon usually stay in salt water**

The paragraph explains that salmon spend most of their time in salt water. It also tells you that baby salmon cannot live in salt water. However, this does not tell you a cause and an effect. Choice C cannot be correct.

Ⓓ **salmon swim to fresh water to lay eggs**

Information in the paragraph tells you that salmon have to swim to fresh water to lay their eggs because baby salmon cannot live in salt water. This is a cause-and-effect relationship. Choice D is the correct answer.

Guided Instruction

Directions: Read the passage below. Use *Before You Read*, *While You Read*, and *After You Read* strategies to help you answer questions about the passage.

BEFORE YOU READ:	• Look for clues that tell you what the passage will be about. • Look at the title and pictures. Make predictions about the passage. • Look at the underlined words in the passage. Read the definitions for each of these words at the end of the passage.

WHILE YOU READ:	• Ask yourself questions while you read. • Look for information that you think is important. • Think about what the details in the passage tell you.

Now read this nonfiction passage. It is an example of a scientific passage.

An Amazing Machine

The human body is an amazing thing. The more we learn about it, the more amazing it seems. Every minute of the day, your body is at work. Your lungs take in <u>oxygen</u> when you breathe in. Then they get rid of old air when you breathe out. Your heart keeps your blood moving through your body. Your stomach and intestines work to <u>digest</u> the food you eat. No matter what you are doing—sleeping, playing, reading, or watching television—your body keeps on working.

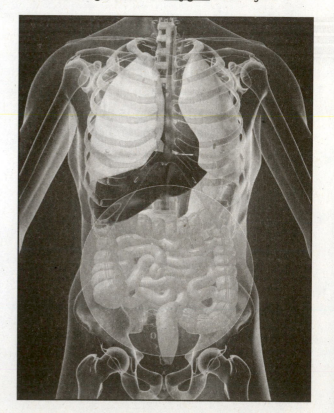

Your body is ready to protect you at all times. Your skin is like a bodysuit. It fits you perfectly. It is waterproof and strong. If your body gets too hot, your skin will sweat. This cools you off. When you feel cold, you get "goose bumps." These raise the hairs on your body to make you warmer. Your sense of touch is in your skin. If you touch something hot, you pull your hand away quickly. The nerves in your skin make you do this. You do not even have to think about it! This is called a <u>reflex</u>.

As you know, you can scrape or cut your skin. When this happens, other parts of your body protect you. Your blood has special cells that rush to the scene. They create a scab to protect the spot and begin healing. When you are completely healed, the scab falls off.

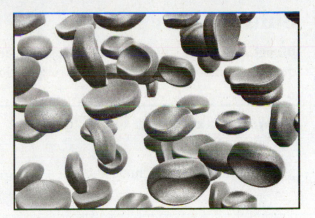

You might get an <u>infection</u> in your body. If you do, there are special cells to fight it. Some white blood cells act like soldiers. They surround the infection and destroy it. What if the same thing attacks your body again? These cells will remember how they got rid of it the first time! They will act even more quickly. This is how your body builds strength against infections.

Have you ever gotten something in your eye? If you have, you might have noticed that your eye watered. The tears help wash out your eye. This keeps your eye from getting scratched. Blinking also protects your eyes. When something comes toward your eyes, you blink. This is a reflex, too.

You can help your body do its work. Your hard-working body needs plenty of rest. It needs lots of water. And it needs good, healthy foods. Exercise is also important. If you take good care of your body, it will take good care of you.

Passage Vocabulary Words

digest – the way a body breaks down and uses food

infection – a sickness; when germs cause harm to a person's body

oxygen – a type of gas in the air that people need to live

reflex – an action your body makes without you thinking about it

AFTER **YOU READ:**	• Think about what you have just read. • Read questions about the passage. • Look for information in the passage that will help you answer the questions. You may want to make a graphic organizer.

Recognize Cause and Effect

Guided Instruction

Directions: Read questions 1–3. Next to each question is a hint that will help you answer each question. Choose the best answer to questions 1 and 2. Write your answer for question 3.

---

1 **What can cause you to get "goose bumps"?**

  Ⓐ touching something hot

  Ⓑ feeling cold

  Ⓒ getting a cut on your skin

  Ⓓ touching a goose

HINT This question asks for the cause of something. It tells you what the effect is. You must ask yourself, "Why does this happen?"

---

2 **What happens when you get something in your eye?**

  Ⓐ Your eyes will blink.

  Ⓑ You will pull away quickly.

  Ⓒ Your eye will be scratched.

  Ⓓ Your eye will water.

HINT Getting something in your eye is the cause. Look in the passage to find the effect. You will need to find information in the passage about your eyes.

---

3 **What causes a scab to form on your skin?**

HINT A scab forms when something else happens. This is the effect. You must look in the passage to find the cause.

_____

_____

_____

_____

Independent Practice

Directions: Answer the following questions on your own. For questions 4, 5, and 6, choose the correct answer. For question 7, you must write out your answer.

---

4 What happens when you touch something hot?

Ⓐ Your skin gets goose bumps.

Ⓑ You pull away quickly.

Ⓒ The hairs on your body are raised.

Ⓓ Your body gets cooler.

5 Why might your body fight an infection more quickly the second time you get it?

Ⓐ Your cells will remember how to fight the infection.

Ⓑ The infection will not be as strong.

Ⓒ Your cells will know the infection is coming.

Ⓓ Your cells will be stronger.

---

6 If you take good care of your body

Ⓐ you will not need your cells to fight infection

Ⓑ you will sleep better at night

Ⓒ your body will be able to keep protecting you

Ⓓ your heart will not have to pump as much blood

---

7 How do your white blood cells protect you? What do they do?

_____

_____

_____

_____

SKILL 7: Compare and Contrast

Modeled Instruction

To compare means to tell how things are alike. To contrast means to tell how things are different. You can compare and contrast many things—people, events, ideas, actions, and just about anything else you can think of.

COMPARING — Both socks and gloves are types of clothes.
CONTRASTING — Socks are for feet, but gloves are for hands.

Directions: Read the paragraph below and follow along to learn about comparing and contrasting.

> Two of Ethan's favorite places to visit are Maine and Florida. Both places are on the East Coast of the United States. Maine is in the North, and Florida is in the South. Ethan enjoys playing on the beaches in Maine and in Florida. In Florida, there are palm trees on the beaches. But there are no palm trees in Maine. Unlike Florida, Maine has very cold winters. Few people spent a lot of time outside after September. In Florida, Ethan is able to play outside even in the winter. It is much warmer in Florida during the winter.

STRATEGY: *Make a Venn diagram to help you compare and contrast.*

The Venn diagram below shows how Maine and Florida are alike and how they are different. See if you can add more details that tell how they are alike or different.

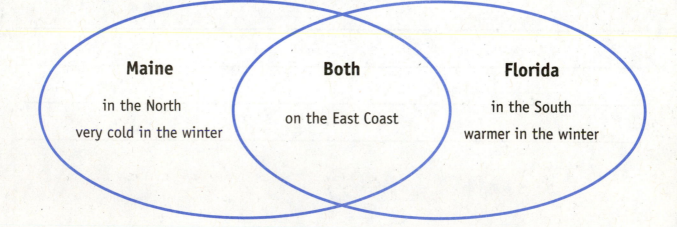

Maine
in the North
very cold in the winter

Both
on the East Coast

Florida
in the South
warmer in the winter

THINK The paragraph states that both Maine and Florida have beaches. In Florida, there are palm trees on the beaches. In Maine, there are no palm trees. This information can be used to complete the graphic organizer.

Directions: Read the paragraph below and follow along to answer a Contrast question.

> A hotel is a place to sleep when you are away from home. Often, people sign up for hotel rooms long before they need them. Hotels offer people beds, showers, and TVs. Some hotels are very fancy. You may also stay at a motel. *Motel* is short for "motor hotel." Motels usually cost less than hotels. They are less fancy as well. They have beds and showers. Some don't have TVs. Motels are often found along big roads. People stop at motels when they don't have time to find a hotel or when they want to spend less money.

1 **What is one difference between hotels and motels?**

Ⓐ Only hotels are near big roads.

Ⓑ Only motels have TVs.

Ⓒ Hotels are fancier than motels.

Ⓓ Motels cost more than hotels.

STRATEGY: *This question asks you to contrast hotels and motels. You may want to make a Venn diagram to help answer this question. Or you can make a list to describe each place.*

THINK Think about each answer choice and choose the best answer. Read the explanations below to check why each answer choice is wrong or right.

Ⓐ **Only hotels are near big roads.**

Information in the paragraph tells you that motels are usually near big roads. This means that hotels could not be the only places near big roads. Choice A cannot be correct.

Ⓑ **Only motels have TVs.**

The paragraph explains that hotels have TVs, but some motels do not. This means that they both could have TVs. Choice B cannot be correct.

Ⓒ **Hotels are fancier than motels.**

The paragraph tells you that hotels and motels are alike in some ways, but that hotels are usually fancier than motels. Choice C is the correct answer.

Ⓓ **Motels cost more than hotels.**

Information in the paragraph tells you that hotels cost more than motels, not the other way around. Choice D cannot be correct.

Guided Instruction

Directions: Read the passage below. Use *Before You Read*, *While You Read*, and *After You Read* strategies to help you answer questions about the passage.

BEFORE YOU READ:	• Look for clues that tell you what the passage will be about. • Look at the title and picture. Make predictions about the passage. • Look at the underlined words in the passage. Read the definitions for each of these words at the end of the passage.

WHILE YOU READ:	• Ask yourself questions while you read. • Look for information that you think is important. • Think about what the details in the passage tell you.

Now read this passage. It is a nonfiction passage that includes functional text. It shows a chart.

Birds of a Feather

A bird is a bird is a bird, right? Well, all birds do have certain things in common. All birds have wings. All birds hatch from eggs with shells. They all have bills. They do not have teeth. Birds are warm blooded. They all have feathers and breathe air.

But bird-watchers know that there are many differences among birds, too. Birds come in many different sizes and colors. Some birds <u>migrate</u>, or travel, from place to place. Some swim and others climb. Some have short, strong bills. Others have long, <u>slender</u> bills.

Birds can be divided into several groups. There are shore birds like sandpipers. There are birds of <u>prey</u>, such as hawks and eagles. There are birds that do not fly. There are birds that climb.

Look at the following information about some different kinds of birds. See how they are alike and how they are different.

	Examples	Nests	Features	Habits	Foods
Birds of Prey	eagles, hawks, owls, falcons, vultures	in large trees or on ledges	excellent eyesight; sharp claws (or talons); strong, sharp, hooked beaks	most migrate to warmer places in the fall	small rodents, snakes, fish, smaller birds
Climbing Birds	woodpeckers, hornbills, nuthatches	in tree trunks or burrows	strong legs; strong, long beaks	often use their strong tails for support while climbing; most do not migrate	insects, berries, nuts
Flightless Birds	penguins, ostriches, kiwis	on the ground	large feet; good runners or swimmers	do not migrate	fish, insects, frogs, berries (ostriches eat almost anything, including rodents!)
Shorebirds	sandpipers, plovers, skimmers	on the ground	short legs; long, slender bills	gather in large flocks, some migrate	fish, sand fleas, insects
Songbirds (or Perching Birds)	robins, cardinals, finches	usually in trees or bushes	short, sharp bills; beautiful songs	perch in trees to sing; many migrate in winter	seeds, insects, berries

Passage Vocabulary Words

migrate – to move from one place to another

perch – to sit or rest

prey – to hunt other animals for food; animals that are hunted

rodents –small, furry animals with large teeth (such as mice and rats)

slender – skinny

AFTER YOU READ:	• Think about what you have just read. • Read questions about the passage. • Look for information in the passage that will help you answer the questions. You may want to make a Venn diagram.

Guided Instruction

Directions: Read questions 1–3. Next to each question is a hint that will help you answer each question. Choose the best answer to questions 1 and 2. Write your answer for question 3.

---

1 **Which of these facts is true for all birds?**

   Ⓐ All birds migrate.

   Ⓑ All birds can fly.

   Ⓒ All birds have wings.

   Ⓓ All birds eat meat.

HINT Making lists can help you compare and contrast. Make lists to describe each type of bird. Look at these lists to see how some birds are alike and how some birds are different.

---

2 **What is one way in which shorebirds are different from climbing birds?**

   Ⓐ Shorebirds have long bills.

   Ⓑ Shorebirds eat insects.

   Ⓒ Shorebirds nest on the ground.

   Ⓓ Shorebirds have feathers.

HINT All of the answer choices are true, but only one tells how shorebirds are different from climbing birds. You can make a Venn diagram to help you answer this question.

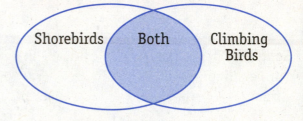

---

3 **How are songbirds and shorebirds alike?**

HINT Review the information about each of the different kinds of birds. Look for information about songbirds and shorebirds. Think about what is the same about these birds.

_____

_____

_____

_____

Independent Practice

Directions: Answer the following questions on your own. For questions 4, 5, and 6, choose the correct answer. For question 7, you must write out your answer.

4 **Which types of birds are most likely to migrate?**

Ⓐ Songbirds, birds of prey, and flightless birds

Ⓑ Songbirds, climbing birds, and birds of prey

Ⓒ Songbirds, birds of prey, and shorebirds

Ⓓ Songbirds, flightless birds, and climbing birds

5 **How are climbing birds and flightless birds alike?**

Ⓐ Both eat insects and berries.

Ⓑ Neither type of bird can fly.

Ⓒ They are both likely to migrate.

Ⓓ Both nest on the ground.

6 **Which kind of bird does NOT eat insects?**

Ⓐ songbird

Ⓑ flightless bird

Ⓒ bird of prey

Ⓓ shorebird

7 **What are two ways in which climbing birds and birds of prey are different from each other?**

_____

_____

_____

_____

Directions: Read the passage below and answer questions 1–7.

A Colorful Celebration

Mr. Gates and his fourth-grade class decided to do something special since it was the end of the school year. Mr. Gates said the class should have a big <u>celebration</u> and invite all the students' families. Everyone in the class agreed that a party was a great way to end the school year. Mr. Gates said that he would bring in food and drinks for the party. Then, Megan suggested that the class should make pieces of art to make the classroom look nice for the party. Mr. Gates and other students agreed.

The next day, the students started making their art projects. Megan and her twin sister, Sara, started making a painting. They found green, pink, yellow, and black paints. However, they could not decide what to paint. Mr. Gates told the sisters they could use those colors to paint a watermelon. Sara and Megan thought this was a wonderful idea. Sara drew a watermelon. Then, Megan used the different paints to fill in the drawing.

Miguel found a box of colored pencils. He decided to draw a picture of his favorite place—the pond behind his house. Miguel got out the green, black, blue, and purple colored pencils to draw the pond and some trees. When Miguel finished, Mr. Gates told him that his drawing looked <u>spectacular</u>.

Elliot looked around the room. All the other students had thought of something to make, but Elliot was nervous about making art for the party because he did not like to draw or paint. Mr. Gates told Elliot he could form a piece of art using clay. Elliot thanked Mr. Gates for his help. Elliot used some clay to form a boat. Next, he painted the boat blue and green. Finally, all the students were finished with their art, and they thanked Mr. Gates for all his help.

On the day of the big celebration, Mr. Gates helped the students place their artwork around the room. Soon, the classroom was filled with colorful pieces of art. Then, the students put the food and drinks on a large table at the back of the classroom. When the students' families arrived they <u>admired</u> the colorful artwork. Everyone agreed that Mr. Gates and all the students were amazing artists. The party was a great success!

Passage Vocabulary Words

admired – looked at and liked very much

celebration – party

spectacular – very good; wonderful

Recognize Cause and Effect

1 Why did the students make pieces of art in class?

Ⓐ to celebrate the start of the school year

Ⓑ to thank Mr. Gates for all his help

Ⓒ to decorate the classroom for a party

Ⓓ to show that they were great artists

REM!NDER

Cause and effect are actions or events that go together. The question tells you what happened—the *effect*. You must tell why it happened—the *cause*.

Analyze Character, Plot, and Setting

2 Where does this story take place?

Ⓐ Elliot's boat

Ⓑ Sara and Megan's house

Ⓒ Miguel's pond

Ⓓ Mr. Gates' classroom

REM!NDER

This question asks you the setting of the story, or where the story takes place. Think about where the characters are.

Analyze Character, Plot, and Setting

3 Why did Miguel decide to draw a picture of a pond?

Ⓐ He was nervous about painting.

Ⓑ The pond was his favorite place.

Ⓒ He had the right colors to draw it.

Ⓓ Mr. Gates told him it was a good idea.

REM!NDER

This question asks about something that happens in the story. It is part of the story plot. You must think about what the characters in the story do and why they do it.

Recognize Cause and Effect

4 **What happened when Sara and Megan could not decide what to paint?**

- (A) Mr. Gates suggested they make something from clay.
- (B) They chose to make a drawing instead of a painting.
- (C) Mr. Gates suggested they paint a watermelon.
- (D) They decided to paint their favorite place.

REMINDER

This question gives you the cause, or reason why something happened. You must find the effect, or what happened.

Analyze Character, Plot, and Setting

5 **How did Elliot feel at first about making artwork for the party?**

- (A) He was nervous.
- (B) He was excited.
- (C) He was angry.
- (D) He was glad.

REMINDER

This question asks about how one of the characters felt. You must think about a person's actions to find out how he or she feels about something.

Compare and Contrast

6 **What did Megan and Sara do that was different?**

REMINDER This question asks you to contrast what two people did. You must look for details in the passage to explain how what they did was different.

_____

_____

_____

_____

Compare and Contrast

7 Complete this Venn diagram to show how the colors Megan and Miguel used were alike and how they were different.

REM!NDER You can use a Venn diagram to help compare and contrast. The center of a Venn diagram is where you list how two things are alike. The left and right sides of a Venn diagram are where you list how two things are different.

Colors Megan and Miguel Used

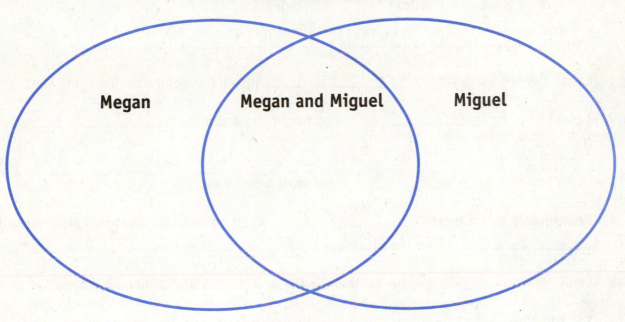

Megan   Megan and Miguel   Miguel

VOCABULARY REVIEW: Skills 5-7

Directions: Listed below are some words that were used in each of the passages you just read. Choose the correct words to complete the sentences on this page. You may look back at the passages to find the meaning of each word.

Afloat in a Boat	An Amazing Machine	Birds of a Feather	A Colorful Celebration
apologized	digest	migrate	admired
canoe	infection	perch	celebration
dangled	oxygen	prey	spectacular
mismatched	reflex	rodents	
oar		slender	

1 Calvin needed some time to _____ his dinner before having his dessert.

2 I picked up the _____ and began to paddle the _____ across the river.

3 Some large birds _____ on small animals such as _____.

4 Breathing is an important _____. When we breathe, our lungs are filled with _____ from the air.

5 Emily _____ her brother for the way that he always helped others.

6 The town planned a _____ _____ for the soldiers who returned home safely.

7 I _____ to Mrs. Evans for breaking her favorite necklace.

8 When it became cold, the bird had to _____ to a warmer place. It could no longer _____ in its nest.

Directions: Some words you have already read in this book are used in the questions on this page. Use what you have learned about these words to help you answer questions 1–4.

1 **Read the sentence below.**

"Manny *dangled* a tasty treat in the air for his dog to see.

The word *dangled* means

(A) dropped

(B) noticed

(C) fell

(D) swung

2 **In which sentence is the word *infection* used correctly?**

(A) Rayanne had a beautiful and infection laugh.

(B) Tommy washed the cut to avoid getting an infection.

(C) Thomas Edison's greatest infection was the light bulb.

(D) People in the South speak with a certain infection.

3 **Read the sentence below.**

"The *slender* snake was able to crawl into the small opening."

The word *slender* means

(A) strong

(B) thin

(C) heavy

(D) sneaky

4 **In which sentence is the word *mismatched* used correctly?**

(A) Nina mismatched her blanket and was very cold.

(B) The students who arrived late to school were mismatched.

(C) Victor was mismatched when he went to the wrong classroom.

(D) The different color socks that Jason was wearing were mismatched.

Vocabulary Challenge

Directions: Choose any three vocabulary review words from the top of page 58. Write sentences using each of these words.

1 _____

2 _____

3 _____

SKILL 8: Distinguish Fact from Opinion

Modeled Instruction

A fact is a statement that *is true*. An opinion is a statement that someone *believes is true*. To answer some questions, you need to know the difference between facts and opinions.

FACT — Ireland is a country in Europe.
OPINION — Ireland is a very beautiful country.

Directions: Read the paragraph below and follow along to learn about facts and opinions.

> My uncle Gerald is a great pilot. He flies his own plane above a part of Australia called the outback. Not many people live in the outback, but it is an amazing place. It is far from the cities where most people in Australia live. The people who live in the outback need my uncle to bring them supplies. Uncle Gerald flies a plane between the towns of Yulara and Alice Springs, which are 200 miles apart. It takes him an hour and a half to make the trip. Many people like to visit the outback, but my uncle gets to go there every day. It is one of the best places in Australia to see.

STRATEGY: *Look at the details in the paragraph. Make a list of all the statements that are facts. Then, make a list of all the statements that are opinions.*

Complete the chart below. Add one fact from the paragraph to the first column. Add one opinion from the paragraph to the second column.

Facts (Things that are true)	Opinions (Things that someone believes are true)
Uncle Gerald has a plane.	Uncle Gerald is a great pilot.
Not many people live in the outback.	The outback is an amazing place.

 THINK Another detail that you *know is true* is that Yulara and Alice Springs are 200 miles apart. Another detail that you may *believe is true* is that the outback is one of the best places in Australia to see.

Directions: Read the paragraph below and follow along to answer a Fact question.

> A superstition is a strange belief. Some people may think that finding a penny on the ground means good luck. Other people may think black cats are unlucky. There are hundreds of superstitions in the world. Most are very silly. But some may make sense. Some people say opening an umbrella indoors is bad luck. It's not really bad luck, but it's a bad idea. If you open a big umbrella in your house, you may knock things over or scratch the walls.

1 **Which statement about the paragraph is a fact?**

Ⓐ There are hundreds of superstitions.

Ⓑ It's a bad idea to open an umbrella indoors.

Ⓒ Most superstitions are very silly.

Ⓓ Many people's beliefs are strange.

STRATEGY: *Read each answer choice. Decide which answer choices tell you something that a person might believe to be true. These are opinions. Look for the answer choice that tells you something that is true. This is a fact.*

THINK Think about each answer choice and choose the best answer. Read the explanations below to check why each answer choice is wrong or right.

Ⓐ **There are hundreds of superstitions.**

This statement is a fact. There really are hundreds of superstitions. Choice A is the correct answer.

Ⓑ **It's a bad idea to open an umbrella indoors.**

A person may believe that opening an umbrella indoors is a bad idea. But this is not a fact—it is someone's opinion. Choice B cannot be correct.

Ⓒ **Most superstitions are very silly.**

Superstitions may seem silly to some people. But other people may not think they are silly. This is an opinion. Choice C cannot be correct.

Ⓓ **Many people's beliefs are strange.**

There is no way to prove whether a person's beliefs are strange. This is not a fact. Choice D cannot be correct.

Guided Instruction

Directions: Read the passage below. Use *Before You Read*, *While You Read*, and *After You Read* strategies to help you answer questions about the passage.

BEFORE YOU READ:	• Look for clues that tell you what the passage will be about. • Look at the title and pictures. Make predictions about the passage. • Look at the underlined words in the passage. Read the definitions for each of these words at the end of the passage.

WHILE YOU READ:	• Ask yourself questions while you read. • Look for information that you think is important. • Think about what the details in the passage tell you.

Now read this nonfiction passage. It is an example of a historical essay.

Water Takes Work!

New York City is the biggest city in the United States. Getting fresh water to all the people who live there is a big job. But you might not know just how big!

In the late 1700s, the city did not have any fresh water. The only available water was <u>unbelievably</u> dirty and <u>unsanitary</u>. It would probably make us sick to see it. And the only way that people could get any of this water was by paying the men who controlled it. The men wanted a lot of money for the water. If people couldn't pay, they didn't get any water. Can you imagine life without fresh water? I think it would be so hard to live without it. New Yorkers found it hard to <u>bear</u>. The dirty water helped spread disease. People got sick and many died. In 1834 a fire broke out, and there was no water that could be used to stop it. The fire destroyed much of the city. Something had to be done.

Finally, a <u>pipeline</u> was built. It brought fresh water from a river into the city. People were very happy. But the city kept growing. Soon this pipeline could not bring enough water to the city. A new pipeline that was bigger and longer had to be built. This pipeline would bring water to one place in the city. Then, more pipes would have to be built to carry the water to different parts of the city and into people's homes.

Building these pipelines was very dangerous work. The men were hundreds of feet under the ground. It was hot and dirty, and the days were long. Many men who worked on the pipeline were killed. The tunnel was finished in 1917. It had taken more than ten years to build.

New York kept growing, and the time came when it needed even more water. In 1929, another tunnel was built. Building this tunnel was just as difficult and just as dangerous as building the earlier ones. The men who did this work must have been very brave. In 1970, City Tunnel No. 3 was started. And it is still being built! Every day, men go down hundreds of feet into the earth. They work under the city in tunnels that are hot, dark, and wet. Today, the workers have machines to

Working on the pipeline.

help them. And the pay is good. But the work is still very hard and dangerous.

This third tunnel should be completed in about seventeen years. That's a long time from now. People are worried about the old tunnels because they are leaking. It is not possible to get to some of these leaks, so they can't be repaired. It is very important for this new tunnel to be completed as soon as possible.

We don't even think about pouring a glass of water. But in New York, the water supply depends on the hard work of many brave people. Every day, they work in deep tunnels that most people would probably be afraid to visit at all. They are heroes!

Passage Vocabulary Words

bear – to put up with; to accept

pipeline – pipes that carry water over a long distance

unbelievably – cannot be believed; very difficult to believe

unsanitary – unclean and dangerous; filled with germs

AFTER
YOU READ:
- Think about what you have just read.
- Read questions about the passage.
- Look for information in the passage that will help you answer the questions. You may want to make a list of facts and opinions.

Distinguish Fact from Opinion

Guided Instruction

Directions: Read questions 1–3. Next to each question is a hint that will help you answer each question. Choose the best answer to questions 1 and 2. Write your answer for question 3.

---

1 Which sentence from the passage is a fact?

Ⓐ "The men who did this work must have been very brave."

Ⓑ "Can you imagine life without fresh water?"

Ⓒ "New Yorkers found it hard to bear."

Ⓓ "It brought fresh water from a river into the city."

HINT To tell if a statement is a fact or opinion, think about what you can prove. Statements that can be proven are facts. If a statement cannot be proven, it is an opinion.

---

2 Which sentence from the passage states an opinion?

Ⓐ "It would probably make us sick to see it."

Ⓑ "People got sick and many died."

Ⓒ "The fire destroyed much of the city."

Ⓓ "The tunnel was finished in 1917."

HINT Read each answer choice one at a time. To find the statement that is an opinion, ask yourself which statement tells what someone believes but cannot be proven.

---

3 Read the following sentence from the passage:

"Soon this pipeline could not bring enough water to the city."

Is this statement an example of a fact or an opinion? Explain your answer.

HINT Think about what makes a statement a fact or an opinion. Ask yourself if the statement tells about something that is true or something that someone believes is true.

_____

_____

_____

_____

Independent Practice

Directions: Answer the following questions on your own. For questions 4, 5, and 6, choose the correct answer. For question 7, you must write out your answer.

---

4 Which sentence from the passage is NOT a fact?

Ⓐ "If people couldn't pay, they didn't get any water."

Ⓑ "The dirty water helped spread disease."

Ⓒ "I think it would be so hard to live without it."

Ⓓ "The men were hundreds of feet under the ground."

5 Which sentence from the passage is an opinion?

Ⓐ "In 1929, another tunnel was built."

Ⓑ "Many men who worked on the pipeline were killed."

Ⓒ "In 1970, City Tunnel No. 3 was started."

Ⓓ "We don't even think about pouring a glass of water."

---

6 Which sentence from the passage contains both a fact AND an opinion?

Ⓐ "In 1834 a fire broke out, and there was no water that could be used to stop it."

Ⓑ "Every day, they work in deep tunnels that most people would probably be afraid to visit at all."

Ⓒ "This third tunnel should be completed in about seventeen years."

Ⓓ "People are worried about the old tunnels because they are leaking."

---

7 Read the following sentence from the passage:

"They are heroes!"

Is this statement an example of a fact or an opinion? Explain your answer.

_____

_____

_____

_____

SKILL 9: Make Predictions

Modeled Instruction

To make a prediction means to guess what will happen next or in the future. Answers to prediction questions are not found in passages that you read. But, details in passages can be used to help you make predictions. You must think about the details you read and then make a prediction.

Detail — Vera picked up her toothbrush.
Prediction — Vera will brush her teeth.

Directions: Read the paragraph below and follow along to learn about making predictions.

> There was a poster contest for the fair that was coming to town. Marissa wanted to make a great poster. First, she painted a pretty green field. Then she thought of many fun things about the fair, such as rides, games, and food. She drew them all using beautiful colors. Marissa also wrote the name of the fair at the top of the poster in fancy letters. She worked on the poster for many hours. Everyone who saw the poster said it was wonderful. When the judges looked at the poster, they all nodded their heads and smiled.

STRATEGY: *List details from the paragraph that you think can help you make a prediction. Think about what the details tell you might happen next.*

Look at the details listed below. Can you predict what will happen next? Write your prediction in the empty box.

Details that you read:

1	Marissa painted a pretty green field.
2	She drew pictures using beautiful colors.
3	She wrote the fair name in fancy letters.
4	People said the poster was wonderful.
5	The judges nodded their heads and smiled.

Prediction:

 THINK Marissa put a lot of work into her poster. Many people said it was wonderful and the judges seemed to like it. Maybe Marissa's poster will win the contest.

Directions: Read the paragraph below and follow along to answer a Prediction question.

> Students today know a lot about food. Some students have learned a lot about organic food. Organic food is food that is grown in a healthy way. Farmers have to follow special laws if they want to call their food organic. Farmers must not add anything to the food that might harm people or animals. They must also treat their farm animals well. Most farmers still grow food that is not organic. But this could change if more people start buying organic food.

1 What would probably happen if more people began to buy organic food?

Ⓐ The food would not be very healthy.

Ⓑ More farmers will grow organic food.

Ⓒ Students will know more about food.

Ⓓ Farm animals will not be treated well.

STRATEGY: *Look for details in the paragraph that will help you make a prediction. You may want to make a list.*

 THINK Think about each answer choice and choose the best answer. Read the explanations below to check why each answer choice is wrong or right.

Ⓐ **The food would not be very healthy.**

The paragraph states that organic food is healthy. Eating more organic food would not make it less healthy. Choice A cannot be correct.

Ⓒ **Students will know more about food.**

The first sentence explains that students already know a lot about food. This is not because more people are buying organic food. Choice C cannot be correct.

Ⓑ **More farmers will grow organic food.**

Part of the paragraph states most farmers still grow food that is not organic. But it also suggests this could change if more people start buying organic food. Maybe more farmers would grow organic food. Choice B is the correct answer.

Ⓓ **Farm animals will not be treated well.**

There is information in the paragraph that tells you farmers must treat animals well to make organic food. So, this answer does not make sense. Choice D cannot be correct.

ONE BY ONE

Guided Instruction

Directions: Read the passage below. Use *Before You Read*, *While You Read*, and *After You Read* strategies to help you answer questions about the passage.

BEFORE YOU READ:	• Look for clues that tell you what the passage will be about. • Look at the title and picture. Make predictions about the passage. • Look at the underlined words in the passage. Read the definitions for each of these words at the end of the passage.

WHILE YOU READ:	• Ask yourself questions while you read. • Look for information that you think is important. • Think about what the details in the passage tell you.

Now read this fictional passage. It is an example of realistic fiction.

Autumn Visit

The trees at the sides of the highway flew by in a whirl of red, orange, yellow, and green. Kiki singled out the brightest trees. She wanted to hold pictures of these trees in her mind. She knew that soon all the beautiful colors would be gone. They would be replaced by bare branches under a blanket of cold white snow.

Kiki loved the fall. She also loved visiting her grandparents. There were so many things to enjoy on these visits. Gran always made delicious homemade donuts to go with the fresh <u>cider</u> they would buy at the apple <u>orchard</u>. Kiki's mother didn't make donuts. She said it took much too long—and they were too fattening! But even Kiki's mother had donuts when they visited Gran and Grandpa. No one could resist them.

Kiki looked around the car. Her brother, Paul, was on her far right. He was playing an electronic game and listening to music. Lu, their baby sister, was sleeping between them in her car seat. Her parents were having a quiet <u>discussion</u> in the front. Kiki wondered if the rest of her family was as excited as she was.

She knew that the first thing Grandpa would do when they drove in was give her mom a big hug. Then he would shake her father's hand. He would probably mess up Paul's hair. He would <u>exclaim</u> about how much taller Paul was than the last time they had seen him. He would tickle Lu. And finally, he would stand back and put out his arms so Kiki could jump into them and be lifted up in a great bear hug. Gran would give her a big hug, too. Kiki loved the way Gran smelled—like apples and cinnamon, and a little raspberry, too.

Right away there would be cookies to eat. Gran and Kiki's mom would go look at the rose garden. Grandpa and Kiki's dad would start talking about baseball or football. But what Kiki was most looking forward to was visiting the apple orchard tomorrow. They went every year, and Kiki loved to see the shining red fruit <u>clustered</u> on the branches. Kiki and Paul would climb up the ladder and pick as many apples as they could. They would drop the apples down to the grownups, who set them gently into baskets. Kiki and Paul always had a contest to see who could find the best apples. And they always chose one fat, red, crisp apple to eat right then at the orchard. Kiki's mouth watered just thinking about that first juicy bite.

After picking apples, Kiki and Paul would select a pumpkin. They made different faces on the pumpkins every year. And this year, Kiki and Paul had brought a new pumpkin-carving kit. The last stop before they left the orchard was at the refrigerators where the cider was kept.

Kiki also liked to take walks with Grandpa. They explored the woods behind the house. Bob, Grandpa's beagle, would join them. Bob used to run way ahead, but now he was getting older. After dinner, there were always games to play before bed. Gran loved card games, and she had taught Kiki quite a few of them. This time, Kiki had a new game that she knew Gran would enjoy.

Kiki felt the car slow down. She looked up. There was the sign for Gran and Grandpa's town. They were almost there! She reached over and pushed Paul's knee. He looked out the window, and a wide smile spread across his face. He quickly put his game and music in his bag. Just around the next bend was the end of their journey.

Passage Vocabulary Words

cider – juice made from apples

clustered – grouped together

discussion – when people speak to each other

exclaim – to say something in an excited way

orchard – a place for growing trees that have fruits or nuts

AFTER YOU READ:
- Think about what you have just read.
- Read questions about the passage.
- Look for information in the passage that will help you answer the questions. You may want to make a chart or list of important details.

Guided Instruction

Directions: Read questions 1–3. Next to each question is a hint that will help you answer each question. Choose the best answer to questions 1 and 2. Write your answer for question 3.

---

1 **What probably happens when the family arrives at Gran and Grandpa's house?**

Ⓐ Grandpa will make donuts.

Ⓑ Gran and Grandpa will greet them.

Ⓒ They will have to look for Gran and Grandpa.

Ⓓ Grandpa and Kiki's dad will play baseball.

HINT Do not look for the answer in the passage. Instead look for information that will help you to make a prediction. Find details in the passage that you think might be able to help you answer the question. What do these details suggest will happen?

---

2 **After apple picking, but before they leave the orchard, Kiki's family will probably**

Ⓐ buy cider to go with Gran's donuts

Ⓑ climb the apple trees

Ⓒ take a walk around the orchard

Ⓓ eat some pumpkin pie

HINT Read the paragraph about the orchard. Look for information in the passage that tells you what the family does at the orchard after picking apples.

---

3 **What will Kiki and Paul most likely do after they get their pumpkins home?**

HINT Read the part of the passage that has information about pumpkins. Look for clues that suggest what Kiki and Paul will probably do with their pumpkins. Make a prediction.

_____

_____

_____

_____

Independent Practice

Directions: Answer the following questions on your own. For questions 4, 5, and 6, choose the correct answer. For question 7, you must write out your answer.

4 From the passage you can tell that

Ⓐ Paul will probably play cards with Gran

Ⓑ Paul will probably fall out of an apple tree

Ⓒ Kiki will probably take a walk with Grandpa and Bob

Ⓓ Kiki's mother will probably help her choose a pumpkin

5 When Bob walks with Grandpa and Kiki, he will probably

Ⓐ run ahead of them

Ⓑ carry his favorite bone

Ⓒ walk next to them

Ⓓ chase squirrels

6 While they are visiting, Paul and Kiki will most likely enjoy

Ⓐ making applesauce with the apples they pick

Ⓑ listening to Gran and Grandpa's music

Ⓒ visiting Gran's rose garden

Ⓓ eating Gran's homemade donuts

7 What will Kiki probably do when she and Gran play cards? Explain why you think this will happen.

_____

_____

_____

_____

Modeled Instruction

Some information in a passage is clearly stated. But, sometimes you need to think about the details in a passage to draw a conclusion. You must put all of the details you are given together and think about what they suggest.

Detail — Kevin collects toy cars.
Detail — Kevin has a poster of a car on his wall.
Conclusion — Kevin likes cars.

Conclusions must be based on the details found in a passage. There may be many details that you need to think about to draw a conclusion.

Directions: Read the paragraph below and follow along to learn about drawing conclusions.

> Luis whistled all day. Sometimes he whistled his own songs. Other times he whistled famous tunes. For his birthday, Luis asked his parents to take him to a concert. He enjoyed hearing the band playing great music. All night he hummed the music. The next day, Luis asked if he could take piano lessons.

STRATEGY: *Make a graphic organizer to help you draw a conclusion.*

The graphic organizer below shows details that can help you draw a conclusion. Read each of the details. What do these details tell you about Luis? Write your conclusion in the empty box.

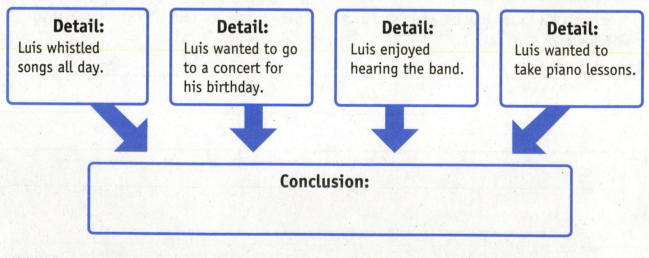

Detail: Luis whistled songs all day.

Detail: Luis wanted to go to a concert for his birthday.

Detail: Luis enjoyed hearing the band.

Detail: Luis wanted to take piano lessons.

Conclusion:

THINK Each detail has something to do with music. Luis probably enjoys music.

Directions: Read the paragraph below and follow along to answer a Conclusion question.

> Long ago, some people who lived in America were slaves. They were made to work all day. Most were treated badly. Many of these people tried to escape. Some used a path called the Underground Railroad. This was not a real railroad. Instead, this railroad was a secret path. There were brave people who helped runaway slaves and gave them places to hide. These brave people were an important part of the Underground Railroad. They helped thousands of people escape slavery.

1 **From reading this paragraph, you can tell that**

(A) slaves were not allowed on trains

(B) the Underground Railroad worked well

(C) people did not mind being held as slaves

(D) no one could escape slavery

STRATEGY: *Look for details in the paragraph that will help you draw a conclusion. You may want to make a graphic organizer or a list of important details.*

 THINK Think about each answer choice and choose the best answer. Read the explanations below to check why each answer choice is wrong or right.

(A) **slaves were not allowed on trains**

One sentence in the paragraph tells you that slaves were treated badly. However, there are no details that suggest slaves were not allowed on trains. Choice A cannot be correct.

(B) **the Underground Railroad worked well**

The paragraph explains that slaves used the Underground Railroad to escape. The last sentence tells you that thousands of people were able to escape. You can conclude that Choice B is the correct answer.

(C) **people did not mind being held as slaves**

The first part of the paragraph tells you that slaves were not treated well. Also, people who were slaves wanted to escape. This means that they did not want to be slaves. Choice C cannot be correct.

(D) **no one could escape slavery**

There are details in the paragraph that tell you about how slaves were able to escape. This means that it was possible to escape. Choice D cannot be correct.

Guided Instruction

Directions: Read the passage below. Use *Before You Read*, *While You Read*, and *After You Read* strategies to help you answer questions about the passage.

BEFORE YOU READ:	• Look for clues that tell you what the passage will be about. • Look at the title and pictures. Make predictions about the passage. • Look at the underlined words in the passage. Read the definitions for each of these words at the end of the passage.
WHILE YOU READ:	• Ask yourself questions while you read. • Look for information that you think is important. • Think about what the details in the passage tell you.

Now read this nonfiction passage. It is an example of a biography.

Helen Keller

It is hard to imagine what life must have been like for Helen Keller. When she was not quite two years old, she had a very high fever. It left her blind and deaf. She was in a world where she could not see or hear. She must have felt very alone and frightened. Some people might have given up. But even at two, Helen was a fighter.

At first, Helen had a bad temper, and was hard to control. She was upset because she didn't know what was going on. She didn't know what people were saying. She couldn't speak to say why she was upset. So she had temper <u>tantrums</u>. She kicked and screamed until she wore herself out. Her parents didn't know what to do with her.

Helen turned seven. Her parents went to see Alexander Graham Bell. He was working to help teach people who were deaf. Bell helped Helen's family find a <u>tutor</u>. Her name was Anne Sullivan. She had just finished school at Perkins School for the Blind.

Annie came to live with the Kellers and began to teach Helen. First, Annie tried to spell words into Helen's palm. But Helen didn't know what Annie was doing. She thought it was just a game. Annie needed to find a way to show Helen that each finger spelling was a word. And each word stood for something.

Helen, as a young woman, reading Annie's lips with her fingers.

One day, when Helen and Annie were at the well, Annie spelled "water" into Helen's hand. Then she splashed water on it. Suddenly Helen knew what "water" was. It was the finger pattern on her hand. And it was what she was feeling. From then on Helen learned very quickly. She was happier and had fewer tantrums.

Soon after Annie arrived, Helen learned to write. She loved to write letters to her friends and family. She kept writing letters all her life. When she was nine, Helen began to learn to speak. Her speech was difficult to understand at first, but it did get better. She learned to read people's lips, too. She put her fingers against them while the person was speaking. This was a new way for people who could not hear to understand others.

Helen finished her regular schooling. She wanted to go to college. Many people thought this was not possible. They didn't know what Helen could do! With Annie's help, Helen did go to college. Her grades were very good. She graduated near the top of her class.

Helen continued to do amazing things. She wrote 14 books. She traveled all over the world. She met many famous people. She gave speeches. She raised money to help other blind people. She did not let her problems get in the way of what she wanted to do. Helen could not have done all this without Annie Sullivan. Annie was called a miracle worker for her work with Helen.

Helen lived to be 87 years old. She once said, "Life is either a daring adventure or nothing." She should have known. What a daring adventure her life was!

Passage Vocabulary Words

graduated – completed school

miracle – something that is amazing and cannot be explained

tantrums – acting out, yelling, and complaining

tutor – a teacher who gives a student extra help

AFTER **YOU READ:**	• Think about what you have just read. • Read questions about the passage. • Look for information in the passage that will help you answer the questions. You may want to make a graphic organizer.

Draw Conclusions

Guided Instruction

Directions: Read questions 1–3. Next to each question is a hint that will help you answer each question. Choose the best answer to questions 1 and 2. Write your answer for question 3.

1 **Why do you think Annie Sullivan was called "a miracle worker"?**

   (A) She could do magic tricks.

   (B) She was able to handle Helen's tantrums.

   (C) She helped Helen to get her sight back.

   (D) She helped Helen learn to read, write, and speak.

 HINT Look for information in the passage about Annie Sullivan's work. Think about what this information tells you. Ask yourself what you can conclude from the facts in the passage.

2 **You can conclude that Helen was an intelligent child because**

   (A) she was very difficult for her parents to control

   (B) she thought the finger patterns were a game

   (C) she learned new things very quickly

   (D) she led Annie to the pump for water

 HINT Find information in the passage that tells you about Helen's childhood. Look for facts about the way she learned from Annie. What can you conclude from this information?

3 **Why did Helen want to help other people who could not see?**

 HINT Think about how Helen felt when she was finally able to connect with other people. Think about the way she lived her life. Decide what you can conclude from this information.

_____

_____

_____

_____

Independent Practice

Directions: Answer the following questions on your own. For questions 4, 5, and 6, choose the correct answer. For question 7, you must write out your answer.

4 **From the passage, you can conclude that Helen wanted to go to college because**

Ⓐ she enjoyed learning new things and wanted to keep learning

Ⓑ she wanted to keep Annie with her for a few more years

Ⓒ she wanted to meet the other students and make some friends

Ⓓ she wanted everyone there to notice how smart she was

5 **Why was the trip to the well so important for Helen?**

Ⓐ Her family was in need of water.

Ⓑ She was able to help Annie at the well.

Ⓒ She finally understood Annie's finger spellings.

Ⓓ She found out what water felt like.

6 **How do you think Helen's parents felt before they went to visit Mr. Bell?**

Ⓐ They were happy with the way things were going.

Ⓑ They were unhappy and feeling that they couldn't help Helen.

Ⓒ They were angry with Mr. Bell for not helping them.

Ⓓ They were grateful that Annie had come to help Helen.

7 **What can you conclude about the kind of person Annie Sullivan was?**

_____

_____

_____

_____

Modeled Instruction

To answer some questions, you must make inferences. An inference is when you make your best guess. You must use details from a passage AND what you already know to make an inference.

Details Given + What You Know = Inference

Inferences are not always correct. But, inferences can be supported by what you read and what you know.

Directions: Read the paragraph below and follow along to learn about making inferences.

> Jill just finished eating her sandwich and rushed outside to play with her friends. It was a beautiful day. There was not a cloud in the sky, and the sun was shining brightly. Jill and her friends began kicking around a soccer ball. Jill looked at her watch and saw that she still had a few more hours to play before she had to go inside for dinner.

STRATEGY: *Think about the details in the paragraph. Then, think about what you know. Use this information to make a graphic organizer.*

The first column below shows details that are in the paragraph. The second column shows facts that you already know but are not in the paragraph. What inference can you make? Complete the graphic organizer below.

Details from Paragraph +	What You Know =	Inference
Jill just finished eating a sandwich.	People eat sandwiches for lunch.	Use the information in this chart to infer what time of day it is.
The sun was shining brightly.	The sun shines during the daytime.	_____
It would be time for dinner in a few hours.	People usually eat dinner when it is about to get dark outside.	_____ _____

THINK It is between lunchtime and dinnertime, and the sun is shining. It seems that it is the afternoon when Jill is playing with her friends.

Directions: Read the paragraph below and follow along to answer an Inference question.

> Many people try to stay away from dentists. They are afraid that if they go to the dentist they might find out they need to have a tooth pulled. Or maybe they think they will find out that they have cavities. But going to a dentist can actually help to make sure your teeth stay healthy. If you go to a dentist, he or she can clean your teeth. This will help prevent cavities. A dentist can also tell you how to take care of your teeth. So, going to a dentist really isn't as bad as you might think.

1 **Which of the following can you infer from this paragraph?**

Ⓐ People should be afraid of dentists.

Ⓑ Everyone gets cavities.

Ⓒ Going to the dentist is exciting.

Ⓓ Everyone should see a dentist.

STRATEGY: *List details in the paragraph that you think can help you make an inference. Then, think about what you already know.*

THINK Think about each answer choice and choose the best answer. Read the explanations below to check why each answer choice is wrong or right.

Ⓐ **People should be afraid of dentists.**

Part of the passage explains that some people are afraid of dentists. But the rest of the passage explains why people should not be afraid of dentists. Choice A cannot be correct.

Ⓑ **Everyone gets cavities.**

The paragraph does tell you that people can get cavities. But it also tells you that going to a dentist can help prevent cavities. This means that not everyone gets cavities. Choice B cannot be correct.

Ⓒ **Going to the dentist is exciting.**

Going to a dentist is a good idea. But there are no details in the paragraph that suggest going to a dentist is exciting. Choice C cannot be correct.

Ⓓ **Everyone should see a dentist.**

Some of the details in the paragraph explain how going to a dentist can help you to keep your teeth healthy. This suggests that everyone should see a dentist. You can infer that Choice D is correct.

Guided Instruction

Directions: Read the passage below. Use *Before You Read*, *While You Read*, and *After You Read* strategies to help you answer questions about the passage.

BEFORE YOU READ:	• Look for clues that tell you what the passage will be about. • Look at the title and pictures. Make predictions about the passage. • Look at the underlined words in the passage. Read the definitions for each of these words at the end of the passage.

WHILE YOU READ:	• Ask yourself questions while you read. • Look for information that you think is important. • Think about what the details in the passage tell you.

Now read this nonfiction passage. It is an example of a historical passage.

The Industrial Revolution

There was a time when there were no machines. Everything was made by hand. If you needed a shirt, you would visit a <u>tailor</u>. He would measure you and make the shirt. But the "Industrial Revolution" changed all that. It began in England in the 1700s.

People began to invent machines. Factories, places where things were made, had large machines and many workers. Factory workers could make things more quickly than people who worked alone and did not have machines.

In a factory, many shirts could be made in one day. But it would take a tailor a few days to make just one shirt. By making more shirts more quickly, factory owners could sell them for less money. Many people wouldn't buy from the tailor anymore because they could get a cheaper shirt from the factory. This was true for all the things that were made in the factories. Machines could weave faster than a person weaving by hand on a loom. Machines could make chairs faster than a <u>carpenter</u> using hand tools. Machines were changing the lives of many people.

Machines made many things easier, but they made some things more difficult. Many machines were not safe. Factory work was difficult and dangerous. And this was a time when children as young as six years old worked in factories. There were no laws to keep this from happening. Factories were unsafe for anyone. They were especially unsafe for children. Many were hurt and some were killed. Men, women, and children worked very long days for very little money.

Workers began to fight back. They wanted shorter workdays, better pay, and safer workplaces. They wanted their children to go to school instead of going to work in factories. It took time, but laws were passed. The factory owners had to meet many of the workers' demands. Children did not work in factories anymore. <u>Conditions</u> improved, but many things still needed to change.

The timeline below shows some inventions of the Industrial Revolution. These have to do with making cloth.

1700	1725	1750	1775	1800	1825	1850	1875	1900

England

United States

1733
Machine for weaving cloth

1765
Machine to spin cotton

Steam engine that runs cloth-making machines

1779
Machine that spins many threads at one time

1789
Steam-powered spinning loom that makes cloth-making faster

1793
Cotton gin, a machine that separates the seeds from the cotton

1870s
Factories and machines are now common

Spinning cotton yarn

Inside a shirt factory

Passage Vocabulary Words

carpenter – someone who builds things using wood

conditions – the setting or manner in which people live and work

tailor – a person who makes or repairs clothes

AFTER YOU READ:
- Think about what you have just read.
- Read questions about the passage.
- Look for information in the passage that will help you answer the questions. You may want to make a graphic organizer.

Make Inferences

Guided Instruction

Directions: Read questions 1–3. Next to each question is a hint that will help you answer each question. Choose the best answer to questions 1 and 2. Write your answer for question 3.

1 **A shirt that was made more quickly in a factory**

  Ⓐ would probably be more colorful

  Ⓑ was probably made with less care

  Ⓒ would probably fit better

  Ⓓ was probably less useful

not sure!

HINT Think about what the information in the passage suggests. You will not be able to find specific facts that tell you the answer. Ask yourself which answer makes the most sense.

2 **How did the children probably feel about working in the factories?**

  Ⓐ They wanted jobs in different factories.

  Ⓑ They would rather have been playing outside.

  Ⓒ They had a lot of fun working with their parents.

  Ⓓ They were glad to be making new friends.

HINT Read the part of the passage that tells about children working in the factories. What can you infer from this information? Choose the answer that makes the most sense.

3 **How was weaving cloth probably done before 1733?**

HINT Look at the information on the timeline. Use this information and details from the passage to help you answer this question.

Before they would be tailors who make it by hand. In the story it says who would go to the tailor to make you a shirt and they would start making by hand. It takes some time.

Independent Practice

Directions: Answer the following questions on your own. For questions 4, 5, and 6, choose the correct answer. For question 7, you must write out your answer.

4 **From the passage, you can tell that if the workers hadn't fought back**

Ⓐ the factory owners would have stopped using children

Ⓑ machines would have become much safer in time

Ⓒ the factory owners would have paid workers more

Ⓓ factory work probably would not have gotten any better

5 **Which of these can you infer from information in the timeline?**

Ⓐ Machines were common in England before they were used in the United States.

Ⓑ Steam engines were used in the United States before they were used in England.

Ⓒ People in the United States did not know how to make cloth.

Ⓓ Less cloth was used in England than in the United States.

6 **How do you think things have improved for factory workers?**

Ⓐ They don't have to work anymore.

Ⓑ They work shorter hours and get better pay.

Ⓒ They don't have to work near machines anymore.

Ⓓ Their children work only when they want to work.

7 **What do you think an early factory worker's life was like? Use details from the passage to support your answer.**

I think an early factory worker's life was hard. Because they had to work in a not safe factory. 6 ages chirland 6 also work in factory's instead of going to school. In the story it says some got hurt or some even died. In conclusion, early factory workers life was hard and not safe.

conclusion

Directions: Read the passage below and answer questions 1–7.

Rich's Day as a Detective

Rich and his sister, Marci, enjoyed watching the *Super Detectives* television show. The detectives on the show often had adventures and searched for answers to mysteries. Rich thought the detectives were very interesting and wanted to be like them. Rich's favorite detective on the show wore a long coat and a brown hat. He also carried a notepad and a pencil to write important notes. Rich wanted to be a detective too. Being a detective would be fun and exciting.

One afternoon, Rich heard Marci yell from her bedroom. Rich ran to the room. His parents came too. Marci had tears in her eyes. She told them that the doll she just received for her birthday was missing. Rich decided to be a detective. He wanted to find his sister's doll.

Rich put on his dad's long coat and brown hat. He also put a notepad and a pencil in his pocket. Rich was ready to solve the case. Rich asked Marci questions about the doll. Marci told Rich the doll wore a purple dress and brown shoes. Rich looked around the room to find clues. He saw some muddy prints on Marci's bed. Rich wrote the clues in his notepad.

Next, Rich asked his parents about the missing doll. Rich's dad said he had noticed muddy paw prints in the kitchen. Rich's mom said she found one of the doll's brown shoes on the porch outside the kitchen door. Then, Rich went to kitchen.

In the kitchen, Rich saw the trail of muddy prints. The prints were too small to be from a person. But, they were too big to be from their cat, Socks. Rich walked out the kitchen door onto the porch. Then, Rich made another discovery. He found the doll's other shoe next to his dog Rusty's doghouse! Rusty was behind his house digging a large hole. Rusty was getting ready to bury something. "You are a naughty little dog," said Rich as he looked at Rusty.

Rich walked behind the doghouse and picked up Marci's doll. The doll was a bit dirty, but was not damaged. Marci ran outside and saw Rich holding the doll. She gave him hug. His parents told him he was a great detective. Rich smiled because he had solved the mystery.

Passage Vocabulary Words

detectives - people who use clues to solve crimes

mysteries - things people do not understand

notepad - a small book to write in

Fact & Opinion, Predictions, Conclusions, Inferences

Draw Conclusions

1 Why did Rich put on a hat and a coat?

Ⓐ He was not sure what the weather outside was like.

Ⓑ He wanted to look like the detective on television.

Ⓒ He knew he had to follow Rusty to his doghouse.

Ⓓ He thought it would help him solve the mystery.

REM!NDER

This question asks you to draw a conclusion. The answer is not stated in the passage, but you can use information in the passage to help find the answer.

Make Inferences

2 Who left the muddy prints in the kitchen?

Ⓐ Rusty

Ⓑ Marci

Ⓒ Rich

Ⓓ Socks

REM!NDER

You have to make an inference to answer this question. An inference is like a guess. Use information in the passage and what you already know to answer this question.

Make Predictions

3 What will Rich and Marci probably do next?

Ⓐ They will look for the doll in the kitchen.

Ⓑ They will ask a detective to find the doll.

Ⓒ They will clean up the doll.

Ⓓ They will buy a new doll.

REM!NDER

To answer this question, you must make a prediction. Look at the information in the passage and think about what will probably happen next.

Distinguish Fact from Opinion

4 **Which of the following is a fact?**

Ⓐ Rusty was a naughty little dog.

Ⓑ Rich was a wonderful detective.

Ⓒ Marci recently got a doll for her birthday.

Ⓓ The detectives on television were interesting.

Remember that a fact can be proven true. Look at each answer choice. Some answer choices tell you what a person may believe to be true. But only one statement is fact.

Make Predictions

5 **What would probably have happened if Rich hadn't found Marci's doll?**

Ⓐ Rusty would have put the doll in Marci's room.

Ⓑ Marci would have found the doll in the back yard.

Ⓒ Marci would have blamed Socks for taking her doll.

Ⓓ Rusty would have buried the doll in the yard.

REMINDER

This question asks you what might have happened if things went differently. Use information in the passage to help you make a prediction.

Distinguish Fact from Opinion

6 **Write one sentence from the passage that is an opinion.**

REMINDER An opinion is what someone believes is true. It may or may not actually be true. Unlike a fact, an opinion cannot be proven.

In the story paragraph 1 it says "Rich thought the detective were very intersting and wanted to be like them."

Draw Conclusions

7 **What conclusion can you draw about what happened to Marci's doll? Use details from the passage to complete the graphic organizer below.**

 To draw a conclusion, use details from the passage and make a graphic organizer. List details found in the passage and then try to draw a conclusion.

Detail:	Detail:	Detail:

Conclusion:

Directions: Listed below are some words that were used in each of the passages you just read. Choose the correct words to complete the sentences on this page. You may look back at the passages to find the meaning of each word.

Water Takes Work!	Autumn Visit	Helen Keller	The Industrial Revolution	Rich's Day as a Detective
bear	cider	graduated	carpenter	detectives
pipeline	clustered	miracle	conditions	mysteries
unbelievably	discussion	tantrums	tailor	notepad
unsanitary	exclaim	tutor		
	orchard			

1 The child had angry _____ every time he was hungry. He was only happy again when he had a sandwich and a glass of apple _____.

2 It had been _____ cold outside all week long. We could not _____ the cold weather any longer.

3 Tia wrote down what she needed to do for homework in her _____.

4 Nobody wanted to go into the water because of the _____ _____ at the beach.

5 The _____ tore his sleeve when he was sawing a piece if wood. He had to bring his shirt to a _____ to be fixed.

6 Mr. Bradley planted many rows of trees in the _____.

7 Gilberto was very happy that he _____ from high school. He knew that he could not have done it without help from his _____.

8 I had a long _____ with my father about the planets in our solar system. He explained to me that there are still many _____ about outer space.

9 Everyone thought it was a _____ when the team that was in last place beat the team that was in first place.

Directions: Some words you have already read in this book are used in the questions on this page. Use what you have learned about these words to help you answer questions 1–4.

1 Read the sentence below.

"When Jenny found her lost bike, we heard her *exclaim*, 'It's over here!' "

The word *exclaim* means

Ⓐ speak loudly

Ⓑ laugh quietly

Ⓒ look carefully

Ⓓ move quickly

2 In which sentence is the word *pipeline* used correctly?

Ⓐ Max hung the colorful flag from the tall pipeline.

Ⓑ The pipeline kept all of the animals off of the grass.

Ⓒ A pipeline of students waited for their lunches to be served.

Ⓓ The pipeline carried water to all of the houses in the city.

3 Read the sentence below.

"The grapes were all *clustered* together on the same vine."

The word *clustered* means

Ⓐ falling off

Ⓑ in a bunch

Ⓒ going bad

Ⓓ in a box

4 In which sentence is the word *detectives* used correctly?

Ⓐ When the TV broke, we brought it to the detectives.

Ⓑ The detectives were used to keep everyone safe.

Ⓒ Brave detectives were able to find the bank robber.

Ⓓ If you are not feeling well, it is best to tell the detectives.

Vocabulary Challenge

Directions: Choose any three vocabulary review words from the top of page 88. Write sentences using each of these words.

1 _____

2 _____

3 _____

SKILL 12: Analyze Point of View and Purpose

Modeled Instruction

A point of view is what a person thinks or believes. A purpose is *why* something is done. To analyze point of view or purpose, you need to put yourself in the place of the author. You need to ask yourself, "What does the author probably think?"

Point of View — What the author thinks or believes

Purpose — Why the author wrote something

Directions: Read the paragraph below and follow along to learn about point of view and purpose.

> Everyone in the neighborhood likes Jake. Jake is always willing to help his family and his friends. One time Jake helped Mrs. Ortiz get her cat down from a tree. Another time Jake helped the girl next door find her toy doll when she lost it. When Jake walks down the street, he always waves and says hello to everyone he sees. All the neighbors smile and wave back.

STRATEGY: *Look for details that tell you what the author thinks or believes.*

Complete the chart below. Use the details from the paragraph to help you understand what the author believes. Fill in the empty box.

Details from the Paragraph (What does the author tell you?)	Point of View (What does the author believe?)
Everyone likes Jake.	
Jake helps his family and friends.	
Jake waves and says hello to everyone.	

 THINK The author explains that everyone likes Jake and how he is kind to his family and friends. The author probably thinks that Jake is a good person.

Directions: Read the paragraph below and follow along to answer an Author's Purpose question.

> Attention people of Taylorsville! The old Sanders Meeting House downtown is in trouble. The Meeting House was built in 1845. It was built by some of the first people in Taylorsville. They met there for years while they made the town the way it is today. The Meeting House is very important to our town. Sadly, it is falling apart! The walls are falling down. The roof is leaking. The windows are cracked. We can't let this important building go to waste. Let's work together to fix it!

1   Why did the author write this paragraph?

  Ⓐ to explain why history is important

  Ⓑ to explain how to fix old buildings

  Ⓒ to ask people to help a cause

  Ⓓ to teach about the town's history

STRATEGY: *Make a list of the important details in the paragraph. Think about what these details tell you. Ask yourself, "What is the author's main purpose for writing this?"*

THINK Think about each answer choice and choose the best answer. Read the explanations below to check why each answer choice is wrong or right.

Ⓐ **to explain why history is important**

There are many details in the paragraph about history. But these details do not explain why history is important. Choice A cannot be correct.

Ⓑ **to explain how to fix old buildings**

The author explains that it is important to fix the old building in the town. However, there are no details in the paragraph that explain how to fix an old building. Choice B cannot be correct.

Ⓒ **to ask people to help a cause**

The paragraph is written to the people of Taylorsville. It is asking the people who live in the town to help fix the old Sanders Meeting House. The author explains why this is a good cause. Choice C is the correct answer.

Ⓓ **to teach about the town's history**

The author gives a few basic facts about the town's history. However, this is not the main purpose of the paragraph. Choice D cannot be correct.

Guided Instruction

Directions: Read the passage below. Use *Before You Read*, *While You Read*, and *After You Read* strategies to help you answer questions about the passage.

BEFORE YOU READ:	• Look for clues that tell you what the passage will be about. • Look at the title and pictures. Make predictions about the passage. • Look at the underlined words in the passage. Read the definitions for each of these words at the end of the passage.
WHILE YOU READ:	• Ask yourself questions while you read. • Look for information that you think is important. • Think about what the details in the passage tell you.

Now read this nonfiction passage. It is an example of a persuasive essay.

A Letter Can Be Better

Have you ever received a letter? There's something exciting about getting a letter in the mail. It makes you feel special. It means that someone took the time to pick out a card just for you. Or they wrote you a note on a piece of paper. Then they put a stamp on it. They took it to a mailbox. You hold the letter and look at it. What will the letter say? You might read it right away. You might save it for later. But it's always fun to see what's inside.

Letters used to be the usual way for people to send a message. Today, many people send <u>e-mail</u> instead. E-mail is great for some things. It saves time. People can keep their e-mails on their computers. They can read them again. It helps them remember what they wrote. E-mail helps people keep in touch. At work and at home, more people are e-mailing other people. People who have lost touch are back in touch. It's easy and it's fun. E-mails and <u>instant</u> messages are a part of life. Many people will never give them up! But there are still times when a letter is better.

It takes more thought and time to write a letter. You choose the paper. There's a lot to choose from. You pick one that you like. You choose something to write with. And the writing is your own. Handwriting is more <u>personal</u> than typing. You can pick out a special stamp to put on your letter. You take the time to go to the mailbox or post office. Getting your letter is going to make someone smile.

And you smile when you get a letter. Everyone sends you e-mail—even people you do not know! You may get e-mails with designs and colors. But a personal letter is special. It comes from someone who knows and cares about you. Someone took extra time to write you a letter.

Some think that e-mail hurts writing skills. They say that people don't use good <u>grammar</u>. They use "e-mail talk." They don't check their spelling. This might be true. But many letters have bad spelling and grammar, too. I think there's a more important difference. E-mail is all about speed. Quickly send an e-mail here. Quickly send an e-mail there. When you write a letter, you slow down. You take your time. You think about what you are writing. You want your letter to look nice.

E-mail is here to stay. But let's keep writing letters, too. If you want someone to feel special, send a letter in the mail. Write a note just to say hi. Send a funny card to cheer up a friend. The best part is that you might get a letter back. There's something wonderful about seeing your name on an envelope. It makes you smile, doesn't it?

Passage Vocabulary Words

e-mail – mail sent on a computer

grammar – rules people follow for speaking and writing

instant – happening very quickly or right away

personal – meant only for one person; shows more feeling

AFTER **YOU READ:**	• Think about what you have just read. • Read questions about the passage. • Look for information in the passage that will help you answer the questions. You may want to make a chart or list of important details.

Guided Instruction

Directions: Read questions 1–3. Next to each question is a hint that will help you answer each question. Choose the best answer to questions 1 and 2. Write your answer for question 3.

1 The author of this essay probably believes that

(A) most people don't know how to write

(B) the computer was a bad invention

(C) people should write letters more often

(D) a letter should be at least two pages long

 HINT Think about the entire passage, not just one part. You must think about all of the information the author gives you. If you only focus on a few details, you may get the wrong idea about what the author believes.

2 With which statement would the author of this essay most likely agree?

(A) People should never write an e-mail if they have paper to write on.

(B) Something means more when you put more thought into it.

(C) It's nice to get a lot of e-mail from people you don't know.

(D) You should only write a letter if you have something important to say.

 HINT Read each answer choice. Look for details in the essay that support each possible answer. Which choice is best supported by the details in the essay?

3 Why does the author think sending an e-mail is better than writing a letter?

 HINT Think about things from the author's point of view. What does the author say about e-mail? In what ways does the author feel e-mail can be helpful?

_____

_____

_____

_____

Independent Practice

Directions: Answer the following questions on your own. For questions 4, 5, and 6, choose the correct answer. For question 7, you must write out your answer.

4 The author's main purpose for writing this passage is to

Ⓐ teach the reader how to write a letter

Ⓑ help people to use better grammar and spelling

Ⓒ tell about a letter she once received

Ⓓ explain why people should write more letters

5 Which point of view is NOT expressed by the author in the passage?

Ⓐ People could be more careful when they write e-mails.

Ⓑ Computers are going to put greeting card makers out of business.

Ⓒ There's something exciting about getting a letter in the mail.

Ⓓ E-mail is great for some things.

6 Which of the following does the author believe to be true?

Ⓐ There are times when we should write letters.

Ⓑ No one should ever use e-mail.

Ⓒ A letter is the only good way to stay in touch.

Ⓓ Writing a letter is always better than sending an e-mail.

7 Give two reasons why the author believes letters are more personal than e-mails.

_____

_____

_____

_____

Modeled Instruction

To answer some questions, you must identify different literary forms and sources of information. The literary form of a passage is the way the passage was written. Passages can be written in different forms, or styles. The source of information is where you are likely to find a passage, or details from a passage.

Literary Forms: a poem, a fable, a fairy tale, a biography, science fiction, historical fiction
Sources of Information: a newspaper, a magazine, an encyclopedia, a storybook, the Internet

Directions: Read the paragraph below and follow along to learn about literary forms and sources of information.

> Savielly Tartakower was born in Russia in 1887. He studied law but was more interested in the game of chess. As a young man, he moved to France. There, he began playing chess all the time. Soon, he had won many games. People began thinking of him as one of the world's best players. Tartakower thought of ideas for many new moves in chess. Some are named after him. He is also remembered for his jokes. During a game, he would say funny things to other players.

STRATEGY: *Look for clues that can help you identify the literary form of the paragraph you just read.*

What type of story might begin with this paragraph? The list of clues below should help you identify the literary form.

Clue 1:
is about a real person

Clue 2:
gives facts about the person

Clue 3:
explains important things the person did

What literary form do you think this is?

_____

THINK The paragraph is about a real person and tells what this person did. A biography is about the life of a real person.

Directions: Read the information below and follow along to answer a Sources of Information question.

> **quilt** \\'kwilt\\ *n* – a heavy blanket to be placed on a bed
>
> **quip** \\'kwip\\ *n* – a clever or funny statement; *vb* – to make quips
>
> **quit** \\'kwit\\ *vb* – to give up, to stop
>
> **quitter** \\'kwi-ter\\ *n* – someone who quits

1 **Where would you most likely read this information?**

Ⓐ in a dictionary

Ⓑ in a newspaper

Ⓒ in a storybook

Ⓓ in a cookbook

STRATEGY: *Think about the information you just read. Ask yourself, "Where would I most likely find this information?"*

THINK Think about each answer choice and choose the best answer. Read the explanations below to check why each answer choice is wrong or right.

Ⓐ **in a dictionary**

A dictionary is a book that tells you the meanings of different words. The information you are given explains what four different words mean. This information would belong in a dictionary. Choice A is the correct answer.

Ⓑ **in a newspaper**

A newspaper has stories about things that really happened. The information you are given does not look like it belongs in a newspaper. Choice B cannot be correct.

Ⓒ **in a storybook**

A storybook is usually full of made-up stories. The information you are given does not tell a story. Choice C cannot be correct.

Ⓓ **in a cookbook**

A cookbook tells people how to cook different foods. The information you are given has nothing to do with food or cooking. Choice D cannot be correct.

Guided Instruction

Directions: Read the passage below. Use *Before You Read*, *While You Read*, and *After You Read* strategies to help you answer questions about the passage.

BEFORE YOU READ:	• Look for clues that tell you what the passage will be about. • Look at the title and picture. Make predictions about the passage. • Look at the underlined words in the passage. Read the definitions for each of these words at the end of the passage.

WHILE YOU READ:	• Ask yourself questions while you read. • Look for information that you think is important. • Think about what the details in the passage tell you.

Now read the passage below. Look for clues that tell you what type of passage it is.

Polly Pitch and the Goodness Ring

Once upon a time, there was a girl named Polly Pitch. People who knew Polly had some fun with her name. They said that it was just the right name for a girl like Polly. If things didn't go the way Polly wanted, she pitched a fit. Her face would get red as she stamped her feet and yelled. If something got in her way, Polly pitched it out of the way. She was Polly Pitch all right.

One day Polly had to wait in line at the market. When it was finally her turn, they didn't have her favorite kind of bread, and the only cheese they had was a kind that she hated. She pitched a fine fit. Finally, a woman in line had said, "Take my cheese, for goodness sake! I can't stand the noise!" Polly took the cheese without a word. "Not even a thank you!" huffed the woman. "Something's got to be done with that girl!"

Polly stopped at the shoe store to get a hole in her shoe fixed. When Mr. Sands told her she would have to leave her shoe overnight, Polly pitched another fit. "What am I supposed to wear home?" she yelled. "Am I supposed to go <u>barefoot</u>?" Mr. Sands put his other work aside and fixed Polly's shoe. She <u>stomped</u> out of the shop. "Something's got to be done with that girl!" said Mr. Sands to himself.

As Polly walked, she kicked the dirt in the road. She saw a flash of silver and bent down to pick up a rather plain-looking ring. Polly put it in her pocket, went home, and went to bed. The next morning, the ring was on Polly's finger. "That's odd," she thought. She put it on a shelf while she ate breakfast. When she was finished eating, Polly noticed the ring was on her finger again. "That's very odd," she said to the ring. "But, okay, you may stay."

As Polly stepped out of her house, a boy on his bicycle nearly ran into her. "I'm so sorry, Polly!" he said. He looked <u>terrified</u>. "That's all right," said Polly. "No harm done." As soon as the words were out of her mouth, Polly and the boy stared at each other in surprise. Polly shrugged and the boy smiled as he rode away.

Then another strange thing happened. Peter Pack's dog came racing down the street, ran through Polly's flowers, and leapt up onto Polly to lick her face. Then he raced away. There were big muddy prints on Polly's dress. Peter came running after his dog. "Oh, no, Polly! I am so sorry! Look at your flowers! Look at your dress!" Peter was ready for a very big fit from Polly. "Don't worry," smiled Polly. "He's just a dog. I can change my dress and the flowers will be fine!"

Peter just stared. He was too surprised to speak. "Thanks, Polly!" he said at last. And he smiled at her.

Everyone was smiling at Polly that day. She liked it! Polly stayed nice all day and didn't pitch one fit. That night, she looked at the ring. "Was it you?" she asked. She smiled as she fell asleep. The next morning, the ring was gone. "My goodness!" said Polly Pitch. "What a strange ring!" Smiling, she got out of bed. It was going to be another good day.

Passage Vocabulary Words

barefoot – without shoes or socks

stomped – banging your feet loudly as you walk

terrified – very scared

AFTER
YOU READ:

- Think about what you have just read.
- Read questions about the passage.
- Look for information in the passage that will help you answer the questions. You may want to make a chart or list of important details.

Guided Instruction

Directions: Read questions 1–3. Next to each question is a hint that will help you answer each question. Choose the best answer to questions 1 and 2. Write your answer for question 3.

---

1 **This passage is an example of**

 Ⓐ   a realistic story

 Ⓑ   a tall tale

 Ⓒ   a biography

 Ⓓ   a fairy tale

 HINT

Ask yourself the following questions:

- What type of information can be found in the passage?
- Why might you choose to read the passage?
- Does the passage tell you about real people and real events?
- Does this passage look like anything else you have read?

Asking yourself these questions should help you choose the correct answer.

---

2 **The purpose of this passage is to**

 Ⓐ   teach a lesson

 Ⓑ   tell how to do something

 Ⓒ   entertain the reader

 Ⓓ   get you to do something

HINT Describe the passage to yourself. Think about why someone might choose to read this passage.

---

3 **Explain how you can tell that this passage is NOT an example of a news story.**

 HINT A news story tells about real events. It tells who, what, where, when, and how. Its purpose is to tell people what is happening in the world around them. Think about how this compares to the passage you read.

_____

_____

_____

_____

Independent Practice

Directions: Answer the following questions on your own. For questions 4, 5, and 6, choose the correct answer. For question 7, you must write out your answer.

4   If Polly wanted to find out more about the ring, she might look in

  Ⓐ a dictionary

  Ⓑ a book of magic

  Ⓒ a news magazine

  Ⓓ a science book

5   Where would you most likely find this passage?

  Ⓐ in a book about jewelry

  Ⓑ in a history book

  Ⓒ in a book about famous people

  Ⓓ in a book of stories for children

6   How would this passage most likely be different if it were a poem?

  Ⓐ It would have a rhyming pattern.

  Ⓑ It would tell about real people.

  Ⓒ It would have more characters.

  Ⓓ It would be much shorter.

7   A realistic story tells about things that could really happen. What are two things that happen in the passage that tell you this is NOT a true story?

_____

_____

_____

_____

SKILL 14: Apply Prior Knowledge

Modeled Instruction

Apply prior knowledge means that you must use what you already know to help answer a question. A passage will have some details that will be helpful to you. But, you may also need to think about what you already know.

When you apply prior knowledge, you make connections between what you read and what you know.

You might read:	Kareem put on a heavy coat and a hat before going outside. He tried not to stay outside for long.
Things you know:	Coats and hats are good for cold weather. People sometimes try to avoid the cold.
Make the connection:	It is probably very cold outside.

Directions: Read the paragraph below and follow along to learn about applying prior knowledge.

> Edward felt like he was sitting under a rock! He rubbed his stomach and groaned. Every year at Thanksgiving dinner he did the same thing. He knew it was too much, but all the foods just looked too good. Edward said, "I can't eat another crumb!" He tried not to move because he did not feel well. Again, he promised to be more careful next year.

STRATEGY: *Connect details in the paragraph with what you already know.*

Complete the chart below. Fill in the empty box with something you already knew before you read the paragraph. Can you tell what is wrong with Edward?

What You Read	What You Already Know
Edward rubbed his stomach and groaned.	A person might rub his or her stomach and groan after eating a lot of food.
Edward was at Thanksgiving dinner.	Many people have large meals on Thanksgiving.
Edward did not feel well.	

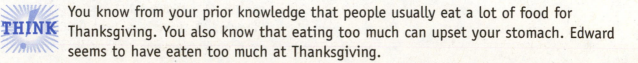 You know from your prior knowledge that people usually eat a lot of food for Thanksgiving. You also know that eating too much can upset your stomach. Edward seems to have eaten too much at Thanksgiving.

Directions: Read the paragraph below and follow along to answer a Prior Knowledge question.

> Beavers are one of nature's busiest animals. Beavers often work near creeks and rivers. They build walls using branches and sticks. Beavers work in groups, and sometimes they work very hard. The walls they build can stop rivers from flowing. The water sometimes spills over the side and floods the fields and forests. Landowners near rivers often think of beavers as a big problem. They try to stop the beavers from blocking the rivers.

1 **Why is it important that people keep beavers from blocking rivers?**

Ⓐ Blocked rivers can be harmful to beavers.

Ⓑ There will be no more water in the rivers.

Ⓒ Beavers often get hurt while building walls.

Ⓓ Flooding rivers could damage people's land.

STRATEGY: *Think about the details in the paragraph. Try to connect these details with what you already know. You may want to make a chart or a list.*

THINK Think about each answer choice and choose the best answer. Read the explanations below to check why each answer choice is wrong or right.

Ⓐ **Blocked rivers can be harmful to beavers.**

Beavers work hard to block rivers. Doing this does not harm the beavers, but it may harm land around the rivers. Choice A cannot be correct.

Ⓑ **There will be no more water in the rivers.**

Rivers will overflow when they are blocked. However, there will still be water in the rivers when they overflow. Choice B cannot be correct.

Ⓒ **Beavers often get hurt while building walls.**

The information in the paragraph suggests that beavers are very good at building walls to block rivers. It does not seem that they are in danger of getting hurt. Choice C cannot be correct.

Ⓓ **Flooding rivers could damage people's land.**

The paragraph explains that a river may spill over when it is blocked. The water will flood the land. You know that people living near rivers don't want to be flooded. A flood might be dangerous and cause damage. Choice D is the correct answer.

Guided Instruction

Directions: Read the passage below. Use *Before You Read*, *While You Read*, and *After You Read* strategies to help you answer questions about the passage.

BEFORE Y O U R E A D :	• Look for clues that tell you what the passage will be about. • Look at the title and pictures. Make predictions about the passage. • Look at the underlined words in the passage. Read the definitions for each of these words at the end of the passage.

WHILE Y O U R E A D :	• Ask yourself questions while you read. • Look for information that you think is important. • Think about what the details in the passage tell you.

Now read this nonfiction passage. It is an example of a social studies article.

Looking into the Past

No one alive today has ever seen a wooly mammoth. But we know that they used to roam the earth. We have never seen dinosaurs. But we know what they probably looked like. We know what they ate and where they lived. Whole groups of people lived and died thousands of years ago. We have a good idea how they once lived. We can tell what they ate. We know of some of the things they cared about. How can we know all these things?

There are the bones of animals and people. There are clothes, <u>pottery</u>, and tools that people made. There are <u>traces</u> of foods. And there are the <u>ruins</u> of places where people once lived. Scientists look at all of these things.

Scientists can date bones. This means they can figure out how old a bone is. This tells them when a person or an animal lived. They look at where a bone is found. The deeper it is in the earth, the older it is. Bones have been found lying in nearly perfect order. But sometimes the bones are <u>scattered</u>. Some parts of the skeleton may be missing. Scientists put the bones back together to build the skeleton. Then they can tell what the person or animal used to look like.

An archaeological dig

Some scientists study what people leave behind. They dig in areas where they think people lived. They work very slowly and carefully. Everything they find gives them information. These scientists can study whole groups of people. They can find where people had fields or farms. They can see what was planted. This tells them what people ate.

Scientists also study how people were buried. Sometimes scientists find only bones. Sometimes they find much more. People often bury things with their dead. Those things are clues. They tell what was important to those people. If the temperature and air is right, even clothing can last for thousands of years.

Two thousand years ago, a man was buried. His body lay in <u>peat moss</u> for all those years. The peat moss kept his body in very good condition. His skin became tough. Finally, his body was found. This man's body gave scientists a lot of information. They could even see that the man had eaten some kind of thick soup before he died.

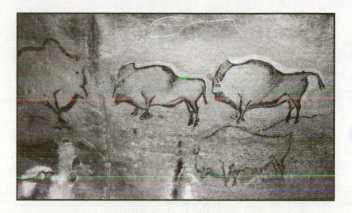

Other things that tell us about the past are art and writing. People drew pictures about their lives. Very old pictures in caves show men hunting animals. The men are throwing spears. Pictures in Egypt show leaders and the people who served them. They show us that cats were very special in Egypt. Sometimes there is writing that tells us what life was like. In Egypt, there is writing from over 4,000 years ago.

We all leave traces of our lives. We leave our mark on Earth. What will we leave behind? What will future scientists find that will tell them about us?

Passage Vocabulary Words

peat moss – a type of soft plant that often grows on rocks or where it is wet

pottery – pots and bowls made from clay

ruins – damaged or broken things left over from long ago

scattered – spread out

traces – very small amounts

AFTER YOU READ:
- Think about what you have just read.
- Read questions about the passage.
- Look for information in the passage that will help you answer the questions. You may want to make a chart or list of important details.

Apply Prior Knowledge

Guided Instruction

Directions: Read questions 1–3. Next to each question is a hint that will help you answer each question. Choose the best answer to questions 1 and 2. Write your answer for question 3.

---

1 **What would be the best way for a scientist to find out what a dinosaur was like?**

 Ⓐ read writings from dinosaur times

 Ⓑ look at a cave drawing of a dinosaur

 Ⓒ look at a dinosaur grave

 Ⓓ put together a dinosaur skeleton

HINT First, look for information in the passage about learning what dinosaurs were like. Then think about what you already know. This should help you to better understand the information in the passage. Choose the answer that makes the most sense.

---

2 **A bone found lying on top of the earth might not be very old because**

 Ⓐ it was not buried very deep in the earth

 Ⓑ it was not very dirty

 Ⓒ it was not near other bones

 Ⓓ it was not part of a dinosaur

HINT Think about what the passage tells you about bones. Also, think what you already know about finding things that are very old. Where would you expect to find bones that are very old?

---

3 **How might putting together a skeleton and doing a picture puzzle be alike?**

HINT Think about what you know about putting a puzzle together. How do you think this would be like using bones to make a skeleton?

_____

_____

_____

_____

Independent Practice

Directions: Answer the following questions on your own. For questions 4, 5, and 6, choose the correct answer. For question 7, you must write out your answer.

4 **Which of the following would probably NOT be found in the ruins of a very old city?**

Ⓐ broken pottery

Ⓑ old toys

Ⓒ old video tapes

Ⓓ old tools

5 **What would be the most exciting thing for a scientist to find while digging?**

Ⓐ a plate that was made 50 years ago

Ⓑ a tool that was used thousands of years ago

Ⓒ bones from an animal that died last year

Ⓓ the wreck of an old car

6 **Which would be the best thing to use when digging close to very old pottery?**

Ⓐ an ax

Ⓑ a shovel

Ⓒ a small tool

Ⓓ a large machine

7 **Why might it be easier for future scientists to study the past?**

_____

_____

_____

_____

Directions: Read the passage below and answer questions 1–7.

Fun with Fish Tanks

Some of the most popular pets in America are cats and dogs. Not everyone prefers these big, furry pets, though. Some people like smaller, quieter pets that can be kept in smaller homes. They like pets that will never run away or make a big mess. They like pets that are beautiful and easy to care for. For these people, fish might make great pets. The best place to keep pet fish is in a fish tank.

With a little work, just about anyone could set up a fish tank. One good way to start is to visit a local pet store. Pet stores will have many things you'll need. Also, the people who work at a pet store will know a lot. They can probably answer any questions you have about how to care for fish.

The main part of a fish tank is—that's right—the tank. A tank is a <u>container</u> or bowl made of glass. That's where your water and fish will go. When choosing a fish tank, you must be sure it has no cracks in the glass. A crack could cause problems for not only your fish but for you as well!

Once you select a good tank, you can start filling it. There are a few things every fish tank should have. One of these things is a filter, or a machine that keeps the water clean. Something else you should add is a lot of small rocks, called gravel. You can find gravel at a pet store. After finding all of the <u>necessary</u> things for your tank, there are still decisions to make. What kind of fish do you want? Do you want one fish or many? Do you want to put <u>decorations</u> in the tank, such as little toy castles?

The last very important decision you have to make is where to put the fish tank. You'll want to keep it away from places that are too hot or too cold. Also, remember how easily glass can break. Be sure you keep your fish tank away from areas where dogs or children play, throw balls, or run around.

Passage Vocabulary Words

container – an object, such as a box, that can be used to store or hold things

decorations – things that make a place look fancy

necessary – needed

Point of View & Purpose, Forms & Sources, Prior Knowledge

Apply Prior Knowledge

1   **What problem would be caused by a crack in a fish tank?**

Ⓐ The fish would jump out of the tank.

Ⓑ The water would leak from the tank.

Ⓒ The fish would become very frightened.

Ⓓ The water in the tank would become very cold.

REMINDER

The answer to some questions cannot be found right in the passage. You must think about what you read and what you already know. Your prior knowledge should help you to choose the best answer.

Analyze Point of View and Purpose

2   **Why did the author write this passage?**

Ⓐ to encourage people to keep pets

Ⓑ to find out more about animals

Ⓒ to gather information about different fish

Ⓓ to explain how to care for one type of pet

REMINDER

To answer this question you must consider the author's purpose. Look for information that gives clues about why the author wrote the passage.

Identify Literary Forms and Sources of Information

3   **This passage is most like**

Ⓐ an article

Ⓑ a folk tale

Ⓒ a poem

Ⓓ a fable

REMINDER

This question asks you about the literary form of this passage. Think about how this passage is like other stories or passages you have read. Which answer choice best describes this type of passage?

Analyze Point of View and Purpose

4 **The author of this passage thinks that pet store workers**

Ⓐ know much about caring for pets

Ⓑ do not care enough about animals

Ⓒ prefer fish to other kinds of pets

Ⓓ care too much about dogs and cats

This question asks about the author's point of view. Look for details in the passage that tell you what the author thinks or feels.

Apply Prior Knowledge

5 **Why should a fish tank be kept away from other pets and children?**

Ⓐ Pets and children do not usually like fish.

Ⓑ Pets and children could break the tank by mistake.

Ⓒ The fish tank is meant for grown-ups only.

Ⓓ The fish tank must be kept in a cold, quiet place.

Information in a passage can help you answer questions about the passage. But sometimes you also need to think about what you already know to choose the best answer.

Identify Literary Forms and Sources of Information

6 **Where would you most likely find a passage like the one you just read?**

 This question asks you about the source of the information. This means you must think about where you would most likely need to look to find the information found in the passage.

_____

_____

_____

Analyze Point of View and Purpose

7 **What does the author think about having fish as pets? List three details you read in the passage. Use this information to help you answer this question.**

 The details in the passage will help you to figure out what the author thinks or believes. List details from the passage in the graphic organizer. Then write what you think the author's point of view is.

Details from the Paragraph (What does the author tell you?)	Point of View (What does the author believe?)

VOCABULARY REVIEW: Skills 12–14

Directions: Listed below are some words that were used in each of the passages you just read. Choose the correct words to complete the sentences on this page. You may look back at the passages to find the meaning of each word.

A Letter Can Be Better	Polly Pitch and the Goodness Ring	Looking into the Past	Fun with Fish Tanks
e-mail	barefoot	peat moss	container
grammar	stomped	pottery	decorations
instant	terrified	ruins	necessary
personal		scattered	
		traces	

1 Everyone helped to put up _____ for the party.

2 Khai took off his shoes and walked _____ on the sand. Then he _____ his feet in the water and splashed everyone.

3 Monique had so many crayons that it was _____ to put them in a large _____.

4 If you have a computer, you can use _____ to send someone a message.

5 In art class, we learned how to use clay to make beautiful _____.

6 The scientists looked through the _____ of the ancient city. They hoped to find _____ of things left behind by the people who once lived there.

7 Some people are _____ of snakes and spiders.

8 Mr. Brown wanted to plant a garden, so he carefully _____ some seeds on the ground.

Directions: Some words you have already read in this book are used in the questions on this page. Use what you have learned about these words to help you answer questions 1–4.

1 Read the sentence below.

"Mattie wrote a very *personal* letter to share a secret with her friend."

The word *personal* means

Ⓐ for everyone to see

Ⓑ not for everyone

Ⓒ fancy and colorful

Ⓓ not very important

2 In which sentence are the words *peat moss* used correctly?

Ⓐ Jenny places her collection of rocks in peat moss.

Ⓑ Lars cleaned his dirty sneakers with peat moss.

Ⓒ After the heavy rain, the air was filled with peat moss.

Ⓓ The rocks along the river were covered with peat moss.

3 Read the sentence below.

"No one could understand Katie because she used very poor *grammar*."

The word *grammar* means

Ⓐ ideas for writing

Ⓑ information

Ⓒ way of speaking

Ⓓ words

4 In which sentence is the word *instant* used correctly?

Ⓐ The students were only given an instant to study for the test.

Ⓑ The cat was so fast that it climbed the tree in an instant.

Ⓒ It took less than an instant for Andy to put on his shoes.

Ⓓ The dog waited for the next instant to bury its bone in the yard.

Vocabulary Challenge

Directions: Choose any three vocabulary review words from the top of page 112. Write sentences using each of these words.

1 _____

2 _____

3 _____

PART B:
Reading Skills Review

The passage in this section of the book is followed by 14 questions. There is one question for each of the skills you learned about in Part A. Next to each question is a reminder to help you recall which skill you must rely on to answer the question correctly.

Directions: Read the passage below and answer the questions that follow. Use the reminders provided to help you recall the correct strategy for answering each type of question.

ALL IN ONE ROOM

Some students love to complain about school. There's too much homework. There isn't enough free time. The cafeteria food is terrible. But no matter how many complaints students may have, going to school is much easier than it once was. Imagine that it's a freezing cold day and you have to leave the building to go to the bathroom. You have to carry a big load of wood from home along with your books. And instead of riding on a school bus, you have a long walk to school in all kinds of weather. That's what school was like many years ago when students of all ages would study together in a one-room schoolhouse.

Many times the local families would build the schoolhouse. They would collect money from their neighbors to help pay for the lumber, nails, and other supplies. The parents realized how important this schoolhouse was. If they didn't build it, their children would probably never be able to go to school and get an education.

Most one-room schools were heated by stoves that burned wood or coal. Students were expected to bring coal or wood to school to help heat the building. One student would have the hot, dirty job of making sure the fire kept burning. And heating the building this way was dangerous. Since the schoolhouse was built of wood, there was always the danger of fire. And there was no fire department nearby to help put out a fire.

There was no indoor plumbing. The bathroom was outside in a little, unheated building called an outhouse. Many times there was no running water in the school. Some schools had a well in the yard. One student would take a bucket to the well, pump water from the well to fill the bucket, and bring it back to the building. If there was no well in the yard, a nearby neighbor might supply water. All the students and the teacher would use the same cup, called a dipper, to drink from the bucket. They weren't worried about germs.

Of course, there was no electricity. On cloudy days, the room could be very dark. Candles, or maybe a gas lantern, were lighted. Again, this increased the danger of fire. This light was not very bright. At times, it was very hard to read.

Life was also hard for the teachers. Like their students, they often had a long walk to school. During heavy rains, the roads and paths would turn to mud. In the winter, they often had to walk through deep snow. At times the roads might be *impassable*.

The teacher would arrive before the students. In cold weather the teacher would light the stove and, if necessary, shovel the snow. The teacher was also responsible for keeping the building clean. And it was the teacher who rang a loud bell that could be heard for miles around. This let the children know that school would start soon.

There were usually about 15 to 25 students. The subjects included arithmetic, reading, penmanship, spelling, geography and history. And the teacher would teach every subject for every grade! Older children would help teach younger children, and many students seemed to enjoy helping in this way.

Because many of the children lived on farms, the school year might last only eight months. The parents needed the children's help in the fields. Even during the school year, some children might be absent for a long time if they were needed at home.

Now that you've learned about one-room schools, what do you think about school today? Have you decided that it's not so bad after all?

Recall Facts and Details

1 **About how long was the school year?**

Ⓐ 10 months

Ⓑ 12 months

Ⓒ 6 months

Ⓓ 8 months

REMINDER

The answer to this question can be found right in the passage. Look for sentences with key words. Read these sentences very carefully to find the detail or fact needed to answer the question correctly.

Identify Main Idea

2 **This passage mainly tells about**

Ⓐ the causes of fires

Ⓑ a teacher's hard job

Ⓒ life in a one-room school

Ⓓ how schools were heated

REMINDER

The main idea is what the whole passage is about. To answer this question correctly you need to think about the entire passage, not just one part.

Identify Sequence

3 **Which of these events happened first?**

Ⓐ The teacher rang the bell.

Ⓑ The teacher arrived at school.

Ⓒ A student taught a classmate.

Ⓓ A student gave coal to the teacher.

REMINDER

Find each of the answer choices within the passage. Make a timeline to put things in the order that they happen. This will help you answer this question.

Analyze Language and Vocabulary

4 **Explain the meaning of the word *impassable*.**

 This type of question asks you to tell the meaning of a word. Think about how the word is used in the passage.

_____

_____

_____

_____

Analyze Character, Plot, and Setting

5 **Teachers in one-room schoolhouses seem to have been hardworking people. Which fact from the passage supports this?**

  Ⓐ They taught children who lived on farms.

  Ⓑ They taught all the subjects for all the grades.

  Ⓒ They walked to the schoolhouse.

  Ⓓ They used candles and lanterns.

To answer this type of question, you must think about a group of people in the passage. Consider the actions of these people and the events that take place.

Recognize Cause and Effect

6 **Students carried coal to school because**

  Ⓐ they were being punished

  Ⓑ they needed the exercise

  Ⓒ it was burned to heat the school

  Ⓓ it was a present for their teacher

Cause and effect go together. To answer this type of question you must find the event or action in the answer choice that goes with the event or action in the question.

Compare and Contrast

7 How were one-room schools different from modern schools?

(A) Different grades were all in the same room.

(B) The students learned about many subjects.

(C) The teacher helped all of the students learn.

(D) Students sometimes helped each other learn.

REMINDER

You can make a Venn diagram or separate lists to compare and contrast things. This question asks you to tell how things are different.

Distinguish Fact from Opinion

8 Which statement from the passage is an opinion?

(A) "Many times the local families would build the schoolhouse."

(B) "Many students seemed to enjoy helping in this way."

(C) "There were usually about 15 to 25 students."

(D) "The parents needed the children's help in the fields."

REMINDER

To answer this question, you must identify which answer choices are facts and which one is an opinion. Facts can be proven true, opinions cannot.

Make Predictions

9 How might things have been different if the one-room schools had not been built?

(A) The children would not have been educated.

(B) The children would go to school somewhere else.

(C) The children would have learned everything by themselves.

(D) The teachers would have come to the children's homes.

REMINDER

To make a prediction, you must use information in the passage to decide what you think will happen next. More than one answer may seem possible. You must choose the best answer.

Draw Conclusions

10 **Why do you think that the older children enjoyed helping younger children? Use details from the passage to support your answer.**

 **REMINDER** To draw conclusions you must think about many different facts and details in the passage. The passage does not tell you the answer, but it does give you the information you need to draw a conclusion.

_____

_____

_____

_____

_____

_____

_____

_____

_____

_____

Make Inferences

11 **The fact that children walked great distances to school means that**

Ⓐ their parents thought education was important

Ⓑ they were needed to help teach other students

Ⓒ they enjoyed having time outdoors

Ⓓ they didn't want to help on the farm

 **REMINDER**

Facts and details in a passage can suggest an answer without actually stating the answer. You can infer the meaning of details in the passage and choose the answer that makes the most sense.

S K I L L S   R E V I E W

Analyze Point of View and Purpose

12 The author of the passage probably believes that

Ⓐ children today don't learn enough

Ⓑ schools today are too difficult

Ⓒ farmers didn't need to build schools

Ⓓ students had harder lives long ago

REMINDER

How the author feels about a topic is his or her point of view. Why the author wrote a passage is the purpose. Details in a passage often suggest a point of view or purpose.

Identify Literary Forms and Sources of Information

13 This passage is an example of

Ⓐ fiction

Ⓑ a folktale

Ⓒ nonfiction

Ⓓ a biography

REMINDER

To answer this question, you must think about what type of information you would expect to find in different types of passages. Each literary form has certain features that are special about it.

Apply Prior Knowledge

14 Why was drinking from the same bucket a problem?

Ⓐ Some people don't like to share.

Ⓑ The water might spill on the floor.

Ⓒ The bucket was much too heavy to lift.

Ⓓ You might catch someone else's cold.

REMINDER

The answer to this question cannot be found by only looking in the passage. You must also think about what you already know to help you answer the question.

PART C:
Reading Skills All Together

There are four passages in this section of the book. These passages are thematically linked. Each passage is followed by 14 questions—one for each essential reading skill. There are also three theme questions at the end of this section. You will need to use all four passages to answer the theme questions.

Theme: A World of Wonder Below the Waves

Theme: A World of Wonder Below the Waves

Passage 1 | **Directions:** Read the passage below and answer the questions that follow.

QUEEN OF THE DEEP

Sylvia Earle has always loved animals. When she was a small girl she walked in the woods near her home in New Jersey. She would play with caterpillars and catch frogs. She made sure not to harm these animals. She would always leave them in the woods.

Sometimes Sylvia and her parents would drive to the beach. She would often play with animals that crawled out of the ocean. One of her favorite animals was a horseshoe crab. These crabs are bigger than most crabs. Many people on the beach were afraid of horseshoe crabs—but not Sylvia. If she found a crab walking along the beach, she would pick it up and point it back towards the ocean.

When she was 13, Sylvia moved to Florida. She lived near a body of water called the Gulf of Mexico. It was like having an ocean in the backyard. The beach became one of her favorite places. She swam in the water with crabs, sea horses, and fish. Sylvia loved the ocean and all the creatures in it.

Sylvia's parents taught her to respect all living creatures. She learned a lot from her parents. She also learned a lot from reading books. Sylvia loved to read and really enjoyed school. She was a good student. By the time Sylvia was 16 years old she finished high school.

Even after high school Sylvia wanted to learn more about the ocean. When she was 18 years old, Sylvia learned how to scuba dive. When a person goes scuba diving they strap on a tank full of air. They breathe the air from this tank while they are underwater. Scuba diving allowed Sylvia to get a very close look at some amazing animals. She could swim next to dolphins and sea turtles. She could study different fish. Sylvia was also able to learn about the plants that live on the ocean floor.

Sylvia Earle graduated from college and continued to look for ways to get as close as possible to the animals in the ocean. She once stayed underwater in a small *chamber* for two weeks. She shared this small chamber with four other women. Together they learned a lot about the ocean. Soon after this Sylvia became well known. She wrote books and papers about the things she saw and learned.

In 1979 Sylvia did something no one else had ever done. She went deeper into the ocean by herself than anyone else. Sylvia dove 1,250 feet beneath the surface of the ocean. She walked on the floor of the Pacific Ocean near Hawaii for over two hours. This dive made Sylvia Earle famous. She became known as "Queen of the Deep" and "Her Deepness."

During her life, Sylvia Earle has spent more than 6,000 hours underwater. She has helped us all learn about the ocean. She has also worked with many people to help protect the creatures that live in the ocean. Sylvia Earle is a very caring and talented person.

Sylvia Earle compares the ocean to outer space. They are alike in at least one way. There is still so much to explore. However, they are also very different. When exploring the ocean there is life all around. When exploring space there is no life around.

Today, Sylvia continues to study the ocean just as she did when she was a child. She shares what she learns with others. She remembers what her parents taught her about having respect for all creatures.

"Every time I went out in the ocean with a scuba tank, I saw things that weren't in books. I can still do it. It's still that unexplored. The oceans are still virtually unknown."

– Sylvia Earle

---

1 **Where did Sylvia move to when she was 13 years old?**

Ⓐ New Jersey

Ⓑ Florida

Ⓒ Mexico

Ⓓ Hawaii

2 **This passage is mostly about**

Ⓐ the things Sylvia Earle has done

Ⓑ how Sylvia Earle learned to scuba dive

Ⓒ where Sylvia Earle use to live

Ⓓ why Sylvia Earle wrote books

3 **Which of the following happened first?**

Ⓐ Sylvia Earle lived underwater for two weeks.

Ⓑ Sylvia Earle walked on the floor of the Pacific Ocean.

Ⓒ Sylvia Earle learned to respect all living creatures.

Ⓓ Sylvia Earle learned how to scuba dive.

4 **In this passage, the word *chamber* means**

Ⓐ a room

Ⓑ a hotel

Ⓒ a tank of air

Ⓓ a diving suit

5 Sylvia Earle is

Ⓐ a sailor

Ⓑ a fisherman

Ⓒ an explorer

Ⓓ an artist

6 Why did people start calling Sylvia Earle "Queen of the Deep"?

_____

_____

_____

_____

_____

_____

7 How was living in Florida different for Sylvia than living in New Jersey?

Ⓐ When she lived in New Jersey she could not go to the beach.

Ⓑ When she lived in Florida she was closer to the beach.

Ⓒ When she lived in New Jersey she never saw a horseshoe crab.

Ⓓ When she lived in Florida she never saw animals that lived in the ocean.

8 Which statement from the passage is an opinion?

Ⓐ "Sylvia Earle has always loved animals."

Ⓑ "Sylvia loved to read and really enjoyed school."

Ⓒ "Sylvia Earle is a very caring and talented person."

Ⓓ "Sylvia's parents taught her to respect all living creatures."

9 Which of the following will most likely happen?

Ⓐ Sylvia Earle will go to high school to learn more.

Ⓑ Sylvia Earle will continue to share what she has learned.

Ⓒ People will forget who Sylvia Earle is.

Ⓓ People will forget what Sylvia Earle has done.

10 Why does Sylvia Earle think the ocean is like outer space?

Ⓐ So much of the ocean and outer space have not been explored.

Ⓑ Most of the ocean and outer space have already been explored.

Ⓒ There is life all around in the ocean and in outer space.

Ⓓ There is no life in the ocean or in outer space.

11 Why do you think Sylvia Earle wanted to learn how to scuba dive? Use details from the passage to support your answer.

_____

_____

_____

_____

_____

_____

_____

_____

_____

_____

12 Read the lines below that tell what Sylvia Earle once said.

"Every time I went out in the ocean with a scuba tank, I saw things that weren't in books. I can still do it. It's still that unexplored. The oceans are still virtually unknown."

What do these lines from the passage tell you?

Ⓐ Sylvia Earle thinks there is much more to learn about the ocean.

Ⓑ Sylvia Earle thinks everyone should learn to scuba dive.

Ⓒ Sylvia Earle thinks you cannot learn from reading books.

Ⓓ Sylvia Earle does not like to read books.

13 To learn more about animals that live in the ocean you would read a book titled

Ⓐ _The History of the World_

Ⓑ _Learning How to Sail a Boat_

Ⓒ _All about Fish_

Ⓓ _Ocean Maps_

14 Which of the following animals would Sylvia Earle most likely want to learn about?

Ⓐ a sea turtle

Ⓑ a zebra

Ⓒ an owl

Ⓓ a butterfly

Passage 2

It was early in the morning. The sun had just come up and the water was warm. It was a great day for a swim. Daisy the dolphin swam near her mother.

"Look, Mom! I caught one," Daisy called out, as she swallowed her first catch of the day.

"Good for you, Daisy!" her mother shouted. She was very proud of Daisy.

When they were finished eating, Daisy and her mother swam out into deeper water. Daisy watched as her mother jumped out of the water into the air. Her mother's high leap was an amazing sight to see.

"I can do that—watch!" Daisy said as she left the ocean water and flew into the air. While she was in the air she spun around. Then she splashed back into the water.

Catching fish and jumping high in the air were just a few of the things Daisy learned from her mother. She also learned what places in the ocean were safe and what places were not. The beach was one place that Daisy was told to stay away from. Her mother told her there were many boats near the beach. Daisy knew that some boats could be dangerous. If she were not careful she might get caught in one of their nets.

Later in the day, Daisy became bored and tried to think of something fun to do. "Mom, I'll race you to the lighthouse," Daisy said.

Before her mother could reply, Daisy raced forward with a great *burst* of speed. Daisy was an excellent swimmer, but her mother got to the lighthouse first.

"Keep your chin up, little one," Daisy's mother said. "Soon you will be even faster than I am."

While at the lighthouse Daisy saw her friend, Cassie. Daisy and Cassie were almost the same age. The two dolphins enjoyed playing together. Sometimes Daisy's mother would allow Daisy and Cassie to swim by themselves. But she always made them promise to stay nearby. She told them that they should never go near the beach.

"Can Cassie and I go for a swim together?" Daisy asked her mother. "We will swim to Eddie's cave and back."

Daisy's mom agreed and reminded them to stay away from the beach. Daisy and Cassie raced each other to the small underwater cave where their friend Eddie lived. Eddie was an unusual friend for a dolphin to have—he was an eel. Most dolphins did not play with eels. But Eddie could make Daisy and Cassie laugh. In return Daisy and Cassie protected Eddie from the big fish.

Eddie came out, and the three friends swam near Eddie's cave. First, they played tag. Then, they played hide-and-seek. Eddie was very good at hide-and-seek. Because of his size he could squeeze into the smallest places. When it was Daisy's turn, she went looking for a good place to hide. She heard the sound of children playing. Daisy swam closer to get a better look.

Soon Daisy was close enough to see the children. They looked like they were having so much fun. Daisy swam toward the beach to get even closer to the children. One of the girls saw Daisy and climbed on her back for a ride. Daisy had just as much fun as the girl.

After taking a few more children for a ride, Daisy wanted to show them how high she could jump. She swam a few feet away from the children then stopped. Just as she was about to leap up out of the water and into the sky she felt something wrap around her. It was a fishing net! Daisy was tangled in the net and could not get out. She was very scared.

Daisy felt the net begin to pull her up. Just as she was about to be lifted out of the water, Daisy saw her mother racing towards her. Daisy's mother arrived just in time. She used her sharp teeth to tear open the net and free Daisy.

"I'm sorry, Mom," Daisy said. "I just wanted to have fun. I promise it will never happen again."

Her mother was glad that she had Daisy back. Together they swam towards the lighthouse. Cassie and Eddie joined them. Everyone was happy that Daisy was safe.

1 **Who did Daisy see at the lighthouse?**

Ⓐ Cassie

Ⓑ Eddie

Ⓒ a little girl

Ⓓ a little boy

2 **Which of the following would be a good title for this story?**

Ⓐ "Daisy Makes a New Friend"

Ⓑ "Daisy Gets Lost"

Ⓒ "Daisy Has Fun at the Beach"

Ⓓ "Daisy Learns a Lesson"

3 Which event belongs in the empty box?

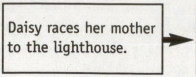

| Daisy races her mother to the lighthouse. | → | | → | Daisy plays tag with her friends. |

Ⓐ Daisy catches a fish.

Ⓑ Daisy and Cassie go for a swim together.

Ⓒ Daisy looks for a place to hide.

Ⓓ Daisy tells her mother she is sorry.

4 Read the different meanings for the word *burst*.

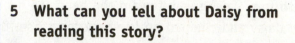

> 1. to start suddenly
> 2. to break into pieces
> 3. to come apart
> 4. to crack open

Which meaning best fits the way the word *burst* is used in the story?

Ⓐ meaning 1

Ⓑ meaning 2

Ⓒ meaning 3

Ⓓ meaning 4

5 What can you tell about Daisy from reading this story?

Ⓐ She likes to get into trouble.

Ⓑ She likes to have fun.

Ⓒ She does not like to play games.

Ⓓ She does not like the ocean.

6 What happens when Daisy swims near the beach?

Ⓐ She gets lost.

Ⓑ She gets too tired to swim.

Ⓒ She gets caught in a net.

Ⓓ She gets stuck in the sand.

7 **What are three ways that Daisy and Cassie are alike? Use details from the story to explain your answer.**

_____

_____

_____

_____

_____

_____

_____

_____

_____

_____

8 **Which statement from the story is a fact?**

(A) "It was a great day for a swim."

(B) "Daisy was an excellent swimmer."

(C) "Daisy was tangled in the net and could not get out."

(D) "Her mother's high leap was an amazing sight to see."

9 **The next time Daisy plays with her friends she will probably NOT**

(A) play hide-and-seek

(B) play tag

(C) swim near the lighthouse

(D) swim near the beach

10 **From reading this story you can tell that**

(A) Eddie is very small

(B) Cassie is Daisy's sister

(C) Daisy is afraid of people

(D) Cassie is older than Daisy

11 **How does Daisy's mother feel after she rescues Daisy from the net?**

(A) She is angry at Daisy.

(B) She is happy that Daisy is safe.

(C) She is proud of herself for saving Daisy.

(D) She is proud of Daisy for swimming so fast.

ALL TOGETHER

12 What lesson does this story teach?

   Ⓐ Children should listen to their parents.

   Ⓑ It is not safe to swim in the ocean.

   Ⓒ Children should not swim near dolphins.

   Ⓓ It is not safe to play games in the ocean.

13 How do you know that this is NOT a true story?

_____

_____

_____

_____

_____

_____

_____

14 What kind of boat did Daisy think was dangerous?

   Ⓐ a sail boat

   Ⓑ a toy boat

   Ⓒ a fishing boat

   Ⓓ a row boat

Passage 3 | **Directions:** Read the passage below and answer the questions that follow.

DID YOU KNOW?

About 71 percent of earth is covered by water. That means there is almost three times as much water as land. Some of the most amazing animals in the world can be found in the ocean. There is still so much that we do not know about them. But we are learning more and more about these animals every day. Here are just a few interesting facts you might not have known.

WHALES

Did you know that whales are not fish? They may look like fish in many ways, but they are not. Unlike fish, whales need to breathe air. They breathe air through a blowhole on their back. Believe it or not, a dolphin is a type of whale. A whale breathes in air through its blowhole. Some whales can stay underwater for longer than one hour before they have to come up for air. So if whales are not fish, what are they? They are mammals. Monkeys, cats, dogs, and people are also mammals. These animals are mammals because they breathe air, do not lay eggs, and the babies drink the mother's milk. They also have hair at some point in their life—even whales! Before a whale is born it has some hair on its body. As a whale grows it loses this hair. So, a whale is really more like a person than a fish.

SHARKS

Did you know that sharks do not have any bones in their body? They do have a skeleton. But the skeleton of a shark is made of cartilage. Cartilage looks like bone, but it can bend more easily. People have cartilage in their ears and nose. If you would like to know what cartilage feels like, just use your hand to wiggle your ear. Sharks are one of the few fish that do not have any bones. There are over 350 different kinds of sharks. Some sharks are more than 40 feet in length. Some sharks are less than 1 foot long. But none of these sharks has a single bone in their body.

TURTLES

Did you know that there are two major groups of turtles? There are land turtles and sea turtles. Land turtles live mostly on land. They have four legs and a head that can be pulled inside their shell for protection. Sea turtles live mostly in the water. Because they live in the water their body is different from a land turtle. Sea turtles have flippers, not legs. A sea turtle cannot pull its flippers inside its shell. For the most part, the only time sea turtles come on land is to lay eggs in the sand. When the eggs hatch, the baby sea turtles crawl to the ocean where they will spend the rest of their lives. Sea turtles are very good swimmers. However, since they are reptiles, they do need to breathe air. Some sea turtles can stay underwater for up to five hours before coming up for air! As you can see, land turtles and sea turtles are very different.

EELS

Did you know that eels are fish? They may look like a snake, but they are a type of fish. An eel has a long and skinny body just like a snake. But there is little else about these two animals that is alike. A snake is a reptile and must breathe air. An eel is a fish and can stay underwater without coming up for air. Eels usually do not grow to be more than three or four feet in length. Snakes can grow to be much longer. There are over 600 different kinds of eels. Most eels live in the ocean, but some also live in rivers and lakes. Unlike snakes, eels cannot survive outside the water.

OCTOPUSES

Did you know that an octopus could change color? This usually happens when an octopus is in danger. **By changing color, an octopus can blend with its surroundings.** Most people know that an octopus has eight arms. But did you know that if an octopus lost an arm it would grow back? There are so many interesting things about octopuses. An octopus has three hearts to pump blood through its body. It also has one of the most developed brains of all the animals in the ocean. Sadly for the octopus, it also has one of the shortest lives. Most octopuses do not live more than three years.

There are so many amazing creatures in the ocean. From fish, to mammals, to reptiles, and beyond—there is so much to be learned. Much can be learned from reading books. But even more can be learned by exploring the ocean. There are many people who have explored the ocean. They have written many books and gathered much information. Hopefully we will learn even more in the years ahead.

1 **Which type of animal is NOT mentioned in this passage?**

   Ⓐ fish

   Ⓑ reptile

   Ⓒ mammal

   Ⓓ insect

2 **Which fact belongs in the section of the passage about sharks?**

   Ⓐ Most fish have bones inside their body.

   Ⓑ Most reptiles lay eggs.

   Ⓒ Most mammals live on the land.

   Ⓓ Most animals can breathe air.

3 **Which set of details from the passage are in the correct order?**

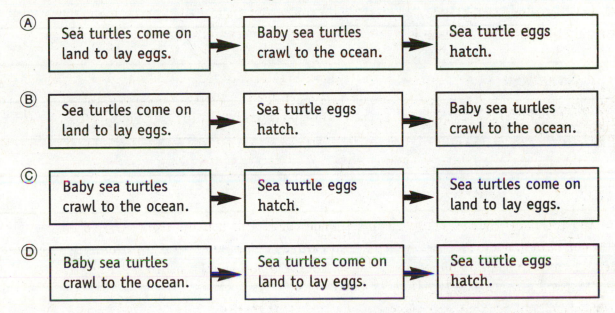

Ⓐ Sea turtles come on land to lay eggs. → Baby sea turtles crawl to the ocean. → Sea turtle eggs hatch.

Ⓑ Sea turtles come on land to lay eggs. → Sea turtle eggs hatch. → Baby sea turtles crawl to the ocean.

Ⓒ Baby sea turtles crawl to the ocean. → Sea turtle eggs hatch. → Sea turtles come on land to lay eggs.

Ⓓ Baby sea turtles crawl to the ocean. → Sea turtles come on land to lay eggs. → Sea turtle eggs hatch.

4 **Read the sentence below.**

   "By changing color an octopus can blend with its surroundings."

   What does this sentence tell the reader?

   Ⓐ An octopus is difficult to see when it changes color.

   Ⓑ An octopus is easier to see when it changes color.

   Ⓒ An octopus can swim faster when it changes color.

   Ⓓ An octopus cannot swim when it changes color.

5 **Where do sea turtles lay their eggs?**

   Ⓐ in the ocean

   Ⓑ in a river

   Ⓒ on the beach

   Ⓓ near a mountain

6 What happens when an octopus loses one of its arms?

Ⓐ The arm changes color.

Ⓑ The arm grows back.

Ⓒ The octopus dies.

Ⓓ The octopus cannot swim.

7 How are eels different from snakes? Use details from the passage to explain your answer.

_____

_____

_____

_____

_____

_____

_____

_____

_____

_____

8 Which sentence from the passage states an opinion?

Ⓐ "Believe it or not, a dolphin is a type of whale."

Ⓑ "Sharks are one of the few fish that do not have any bones."

Ⓒ "Some of the most amazing animals in the world can be found in the ocean."

Ⓓ "Eels usually do not grow to be more than three or four feet in length."

9 What must a whale do after swimming underwater?

   Ⓐ rest at the bottom of the ocean

   Ⓑ swim to the surface to breathe air

   Ⓒ eat fish and drink water

   Ⓓ lay eggs in the sand

10 What can you tell from reading this passage?

   Ⓐ All sharks look the same.

   Ⓑ A dolphin does not need to breathe air.

   Ⓒ Not all turtles live in the ocean.

   Ⓓ An octopus can have more than eight arms.

11 A whale is more like a person than a fish because

   Ⓐ it can swim

   Ⓑ it has a blowhole

   Ⓒ it has bones

   Ⓓ it breathes air

12 The person who wrote this passage most likely thinks

   Ⓐ we should try to learn more about the ocean

   Ⓑ we do not have to explore the ocean if we read books

   Ⓒ there are not many animals that live in the ocean

   Ⓓ the only animals that live in the ocean are fish

13 How could you learn more about the animals in this passage? Tell what kinds of books you could read or places you could visit.

_____

_____

_____

_____

_____

_____

_____

14 A turtle's shell is most like

   Ⓐ a motor in a car

   Ⓑ a roof on a house

   Ⓒ a feather in a pillow

   Ⓓ a sail on a boat

ALL TOGETHER

Passage 4

July 14, 2003

Dear Ben,

How is everything back home? How are Mom and Dad? The Bahaman Islands are great! Uncle Leo and I are staying on an island called Grand Bahama. It is only about 70 miles from Florida. It is always warm and there is so much to do.

On the day that Uncle Leo and I arrived, we went to the beach. The water here is so clear. I can see my feet even when I am standing in water above my waist. The best part about the clear water is that you can see the pretty fish. The fish here are awesome! It reminds me of Hawaii. Some are bright red, some are orange, and some are even purple and yellow.

I wish you could have come with us. Maybe when you are older Mom and Dad will let you visit the Bahamas with Uncle Leo. I took some great pictures. I will show them to you when I get back to Kansas.

On our second day here we went sailing, and the next day Uncle Leo took me fishing.

Uncle Leo caught a big fish called a marlin. I helped him reel it in. The fish was almost four feet long. We took a picture of the two of us holding the fish, and then we returned it to the ocean. On our way back to shore, a pod of dolphins swam next to the boat. A pod is what you call a group of dolphins. The man who drove the boat told us some dolphins like to swim with people. He told us where we could go to swim with dolphins.

Uncle Leo and I went to the place that the man on the boat told us about. When it was our turn to swim with the dolphins, we went out into the water with a dolphin trainer named Keisha. She knew everything about dolphins. She told us that we would be swimming with trained dolphins. Keisha said that it was not a good idea to swim with dolphins that were not trained to be around people. Even though dolphins are friendly, if they are scared they might bite a person. A trained dolphin is not be as likely to be scared.

After Keisha told us everything we needed to know, we were allowed to swim with a dolphin named Sophie. Sophie was such a sweet and gentle dolphin. Keisha showed us how to ride on Sophie's back. She also showed us how to reward Sophie by feeding her fish. Keisha explained that it was important to reward dolphins. Without rewards it would be difficult to train dolphins. Keisha was kind enough to take a picture of Uncle Leo and me with Sophie. I can't wait to show it to you.

Yesterday was another great day. Uncle Leo and I went snorkeling. You wear a mask and get air by breathing through a tube. The tube is not very long so you must stay near the surface of the water. You float on your stomach and look down at all the colorful sea creatures. It was fun and exciting. I felt like I was swimming in a fish tank. We even saw some sea stars. Uncle Leo said that is what you should call a starfish since it is really not a fish at all. I always thought sea stars had five arms. But we found some that had more than five arms. I found one that had ten arms!

Today, Uncle Leo is going to teach me how to water ski. I don't think it's as easy as it looks. I'll let you know how I did when I get home on Saturday. I'll see you in three days!

From your big sister,

April

ALL TOGETHER

1 Where does April live?

Ⓐ Florida

Ⓑ Grand Bahama

Ⓒ Kansas

Ⓓ Hawaii

2 This letter tells mostly about

Ⓐ what April did while on vacation

Ⓑ the Bahaman Islands

Ⓒ why dolphins need to be trained

Ⓓ who Leo is

3 List three things April did while on vacation in the order that she did them.

_____

_____

_____

_____

_____

_____

4 What words in the passage help the reader to know what the word *reel* means?

Ⓐ *sailing* and *fishing*

Ⓑ *picture* and *holding*

Ⓒ *caught* and *fish*

Ⓓ *let* and *help*

5 Who is Sophie?

Ⓐ April's sister

Ⓑ April's mother

Ⓒ a dolphin trainer

Ⓓ a dolphin

6 Why might a dolphin bite a person?

Ⓐ It is scared.

Ⓑ It is hungry.

Ⓒ It is lost.

Ⓓ It is tired.

7 What does April think snorkeling is like?

Ⓐ water skiing

Ⓑ going fishing

Ⓒ floating on your back

Ⓓ swimming in a fish tank

8 Which sentence from the letter is an example of a fact?

Ⓐ "The fish here are awesome!"

Ⓑ "A pod is what you call a group of dolphins."

Ⓒ "Yesterday was another great day."

Ⓓ "It was fun and exciting."

9 What will April do when she gets back home?

Ⓐ show Ben some pictures

Ⓑ visit Keisha

Ⓒ learn how to water ski

Ⓓ go snorkeling with Ben

10 What day of the week was it when April wrote this letter?

Ⓐ Saturday

Ⓑ Friday

Ⓒ Thursday

Ⓓ Wednesday

11 Ben did not go on vacation with April because

Ⓐ he is sick and needs to rest

Ⓑ he is too young to go so far away from home

Ⓒ he does not like to swim in the ocean

Ⓓ he did not save enough money to go away

ALL TOGETHER

12 Why did April write this letter?

    Ⓐ to tell Ben how much she misses home

    Ⓑ to ask Ben to come to the Bahamas

    Ⓒ to tell Ben how much fun she is having

    Ⓓ to ask Ben to send her some pictures

13 What helps the reader to know this passage is a letter?

    Ⓐ It does not have many words that rhyme.

    Ⓑ It does not have a title or page numbers.

    Ⓒ Everything that is written is true.

    Ⓓ It starts with "Dear Ben," and it says who wrote it.

14 List three things a person should bring if they go to the Bahamas. Explain why a person would need each of these things.

_____

_____

_____

_____

_____

_____

_____

_____

_____

_____

Theme Questions

Directions: The next three questions are about the theme "A World of Wonder Below the Waves." Use the four passages you have just read to help you answer these questions.

1 **Which animal is mentioned in all four passages?**

   Ⓐ shark

   Ⓑ dolphin

   Ⓒ sea turtle

   Ⓓ crab

2 **What can be learned from exploring the ocean? Include at least one fact you have learned from each of the four passages you have just read.**

   _____

   _____

   _____

   _____

   _____

   _____

   _____

   _____

   _____

   _____

3 **Compare two people or characters from the four passages you just read. Explain two ways they are alike and two ways they are different.**

_____

_____

_____

_____

_____

_____

_____

_____

_____

_____

_____

PART D:
Assessments

There are two assessments in this section of the book. Each assessment includes two passages. Each passage is followed by 14 questions. Completing these assessments will help your teacher to track your progress on each of the 14 Essential Skills for Reading Success.

Passage 1 | **Directions:** Read the passage below and answer the questions that follow.

Sally Saves Her Family

Sally's family went on a trip to the beach. They placed a big beach towel on the hot sand. They put their food and drinks on the towel. Sally's little brother, Tim, ran off to play in the water. Sally's parents sat down on the towel and started to read some of the books they'd brought.

Sally looked back and forth between Tim and her parents. "I don't want to get wet in the water just yet," she thought. "But I also don't want to sit here and read. I'm at the beach. I want to find something exciting to do!"

So, Sally decided to go exploring. The first place she headed was to the top of a big hill of sand. It was a long walk, and the heat made her tired. By the time she got to the top, she had to sit down. Luckily, there was a big black bench there—or so she thought. She sat down on it only to notice that it was shaking.

She stood up and looked at it curiously. It was then she saw that it wasn't a bench but a very large, locked box. And it was shaking back and forth. "What on Earth is this?" she thought. When she heard a sound inside, she just had to open it.

The old lock was rusty. When Sally hit it with a rock, it opened and fell to the sand. Sally stepped back as the box seemed to open itself! That was surprising enough. It was even more surprising when she saw a man climb out of the box!

"Arrrr!" said the man. He was wearing worn-out pirate's clothes. He had a long beard, a peg leg, and a hook for a hand!

The old pirate looked around and stretched his arms and legs. "Thank ye, lassie, for letting me out of there. I must have been locked up for years and years!"

"You're welcome, sir," said Sally.

"My name is Wild Will Whackem," he said. "It's good to be back on my beach."

"This is your beach?" asked Sally.

"Arrrr, it is," said Wild Will. "This is where I buried my treasure long ago."

"But there's no treasure here anymore, mister," said Sally. "This is a family beach. People just come here to have fun."

Wild Will looked angry. "Fun? A pirate has no time for fun. I want my treasure!"

"But it's not here," said Sally again. "My family comes here often. We've never seen a treasure!"

Wild Will stamped his foot. "I want treasure!" he said. "If mine isn't here anymore, I'm going to have to steal some new treasure. I'll rob those people on the beach, arrrr!"

He hurried out toward Sally's family. Sally knew her parents and Tim were in trouble. Luckily, though, Wild Will was having a hard time walking on his peg leg. It kept sinking into the hot sand. He began walking, very slowly, down the hill toward the beach.

Sally thought fast. She grabbed the empty box and pushed it down the other side of the hill.

It slid down quickly while she ran beside it. When it was at the bottom of the hill, she called up to Wild Will, "Mister, I think your treasure is down here!"

The old pirate spun around. He saw a treasure chest, and his greedy eyes grew wide. "Arrrr! That must be my treasure!" he yelled. He began trying to run toward it, but his peg leg made him trip. Wild Will fell down the hill and *tumbled* directly into the box!

Sally slammed the lid shut and snapped the lock tight. "You can stay there until you learn to behave!" she said.

1 How did Sally get the lock off the box?

(A) She hit it with a rock.

(B) She poured water on it.

(C) She found a special key.

(D) She let the pirate break it.

2 This passage is mostly about

(A) a family's trip

(B) a pirate's crimes

(C) a beach's history

(D) a girl's adventure

3 What does Wild Will do right after he gets out of the box?

(A) He thanks Sally.

(B) He falls down the hill.

(C) He stumbles on the sand.

(D) He decides to rob Sally's family.

4 **Read this sentence from the passage.**

"Wild Will fell down the hill and *tumbled* directly into the box."

What does the word *tumbled* mean?

Ⓐ looked

Ⓑ fell

Ⓒ turned quickly

Ⓓ walked slowly

5 **Where does most of the action in this story take place?**

Ⓐ a hill near the beach

Ⓑ a flat area of the beach

Ⓒ the water near the beach

Ⓓ the family's beach towel

6 **What makes Wild Will fall down the hill?**

Ⓐ Sally pushes him.

Ⓑ He trips on his peg leg.

Ⓒ He falls over a treasure chest.

Ⓓ He is surprised by Sally's voice.

7 **What is one difference between Sally and Wild Will?**

_____

_____

_____

_____

_____

_____

_____

_____

8 **Which of the following states a fact?**

Ⓐ "That was surprising enough."

Ⓑ "He began walking, very slowly."

Ⓒ "It's good to be back on my beach."

Ⓓ "When Sally hit the lock, it opened."

9 **The next time Sally's family goes to the beach, Sally will probably**

Ⓐ beg her parents to go somewhere else

Ⓑ ask the pirate if he's willing to behave

Ⓒ let the pirate out of the box

Ⓓ find a hidden treasure chest

10 There is enough information in the story to conclude that

Ⓐ all pirates have peg legs

Ⓑ Tim doesn't like the beach

Ⓒ not many people visit the beach

Ⓓ Sally likes looking for adventure

11 Why did Sally think her family was in trouble? Use details from the passage to explain your answer.

_____

_____

_____

_____

_____

_____

_____

_____

_____

_____

A
S
S
E
S
S
M
E
N
T
S

Assessment 1

12 Why did the author most likely write this story?

- Ⓐ to inform readers about pirates
- Ⓑ to describe beaches in America
- Ⓒ to entertain readers with a make-believe tale
- Ⓓ to ask readers to search for buried treasure

13 What would be the best source of information to learn about real pirates?

- Ⓐ a cartoon
- Ⓑ a fiction story
- Ⓒ a history book
- Ⓓ a newspaper article

14 How can you tell that this story is NOT true?

- Ⓐ There are no hills near beaches.
- Ⓑ Not many families go to beaches.
- Ⓒ Pirates don't really like treasure.
- Ⓓ A person couldn't live for years in a box.

Passage 2 | **Directions:** Read the passage below and answer the questions that follow.

Hummingbirds

What bird can travel as quickly as a car? What bird can move up, down, and sideways in the blink of an eye? If your answer is the hummingbird, you are right. There are three hundred and twenty types of these amazing birds. Once you see a hummingbird, you will never forget that special moment!

There are many interesting things to learn about these birds. For example, the hummingbird's heart beats about 1,260 times each minute. Our hearts beat about 70 times each minute.

And hummingbirds are wonderful fliers. Their wings beat up and down so quickly that they look like a blur. In fact, their wings can beat up and down from 10 to 80 times every second. The hummingbird's wings make a noise that sounds like a bumblebee in flight. Hummingbirds can fly as far as 50 to 60 miles in one hour. Their small, stiff wings give them very good control over their speed and direction. They can change direction instantly.

Hummingbirds are also among the most beautiful birds. The ruby-throated hummingbird is one of the most common, but it is still a lovely sight. The upper part of its body is shiny green. The males have red throats, and the females' throats are white. Other hummingbirds are even more brightly colored.

Some of the hummingbird's favorite foods are insects and nectar from flowers. Their long, thin bills are very good for reaching deep inside flowers to get the nectar. Their long tongues let them reach even further. Their tongues are also great for helping to catch insects.

Hummingbirds take good care of their young. They are very clever at hiding their nests. Their nests are made of bark, grass, and other plants, so they blend into the surroundings. This *camouflage* helps protect hummingbirds from their enemies. Cats, other birds, and even snakes might want to eat them. But the hidden nest is a safe home for the adults and their babies.

Most times the female hummingbird lays two tiny eggs in the nest. If the adult is so small, you can imagine what the babies must look like! The baby birds hatch in about two weeks. They have no feathers and are totally blind. The mother feeds them plenty of insects, and in a few weeks they are ready to fly away.

In the spring, hummingbirds migrate from the tropics to cooler places. The male leaves about three weeks before the female. Nobody is sure why they do this. Some people think the males leave first to look for food. This will keep the females and their young from starving. They also think if the females leave later, there will be more flowers in bloom. This way, they will have more nectar for food.

If you want to learn more about hummingbirds, there are many books in the library and sites on the Internet. If you are really lucky, someday you will see one. Look quickly, because that flash of color will be gone in a second!

1 How many times do the hummingbird's wings beat every second?

Ⓐ about 1,260 times

Ⓑ about 2 times

Ⓒ from 10 to 80 times

Ⓓ from 100 to 800 times

2 What is the main idea of the third paragraph?

Ⓐ Hummingbirds are beautiful to look at.

Ⓑ Hummingbirds are amazing fliers.

Ⓒ Hummingbirds can travel very quickly.

Ⓓ Hummingbirds can change direction quickly.

3 Which event belongs in the empty box?

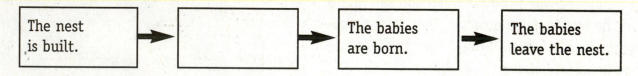

Ⓐ The female gathers grass.

Ⓑ The babies practice their flying.

Ⓒ The female lays two tiny eggs in the nest.

Ⓓ The female chooses a spot for the nest.

4 You can tell from the passage that *camouflage* lets birds

   Ⓐ sing

   Ⓑ hide

   Ⓒ eat

   Ⓓ fly

5 Which word best describes hummingbirds?

   Ⓐ scared

   Ⓑ rare

   Ⓒ slow

   Ⓓ beautiful

6 What would happen if the hummingbird did not have a long tongue?

   Ⓐ It would not be able to escape from its enemies.

   Ⓑ It would not be able to take care of the two eggs.

   Ⓒ It would not be able to drink water.

   Ⓓ It would not be able to reach the nectar.

7 According to the passage, how are male hummingbirds different from female hummingbirds?

   Ⓐ They fly north before the females.

   Ⓑ They can fly much faster.

   Ⓒ They help take care of the babies.

   Ⓓ Their hearts beat at a slower rate.

8 Which statement from the passage is an example of an opinion?

   Ⓐ "The upper part of its body is shiny green."

   Ⓑ "Once you see a hummingbird, you will never forget that special moment!"

   Ⓒ "In the spring, hummingbirds migrate from the tropics to cooler places."

   Ⓓ "Most times the female hummingbird lays two tiny eggs in the nest."

9 What is one thing that would probably happen if hummingbirds were not such great fliers?

_____

_____

_____

_____

_____

_____

_____

ASSESSMENTS

Assessment 1

10 Where will the hummingbirds most likely fly in the fall? Explain how you know.

_____

_____

_____

_____

_____

_____

_____

_____

_____

_____

_____

_____

11 How can you tell from the passage that hummingbirds are good parents?

Ⓐ The babies are small and blind.

Ⓑ The babies are born without any feathers.

Ⓒ They protect the babies and make sure they do not starve.

Ⓓ The female lays two tiny eggs that hatch in two weeks.

12 This passage was most likely written

Ⓐ to challenge

Ⓑ to persuade

Ⓒ to entertain

Ⓓ to inform

13 You might expect to find this in a book titled

Ⓐ _Birds of the World_

Ⓑ _Building a Nest_

Ⓒ _Nature's Protection_

Ⓓ _Feeding the Birds_

14 What do hummingbirds have in common with other animals?

Ⓐ They have small stiff wings.

Ⓑ Their hearts beat very quickly.

Ⓒ They have many enemies.

Ⓓ They are very difficult to see.

Passage 1 | **Directions:** Read the passage below and answer the questions that follow.

GOING SOUTH FOR THE WINTER

Mr. and Mrs. Lopez finished packing their bags. Rose still had a few more things she wanted to pack. She grabbed a sweater from the closet. She also took a pair of gloves from her dresser drawer. Rose stopped packing for a minute to think about what else she would need. She looked out her bedroom window and saw the snow was still falling. It had been snowing all morning. She opened another drawer and took out her scarf.

After Rose was done packing, she helped her parents put all the bags in the trunk of the car. They only had one hour before their plane would leave the airport. It took about 20 minutes to get to the airport.

During the ride, Rose thought about all of the things she wanted to do once she arrived in Mexico. It was almost three years since she saw Uncle Hector, Aunt Tula, and her cousins. She could not wait to play with her cousins, Maria and Miguel. Rose was the same age as her cousin, Maria. Miguel was three years older. Whenever they played together they always had fun.

"This vacation is going to be so much fun," Rose told her mom and dad. "I can't wait to build a snowman with my cousins."

Mr. and Mrs. Lopez laughed. Rose did not understand why they were laughing.

"What's so funny?" Rose asked. "I bet Maria and Miguel love building snowmen."

"There isn't going to be any snow while we are in Mexico," Mrs. Lopez explained. "Mexico is not the same as Chicago."

Rose did not know how her mother could be so sure it would not snow. Even if it didn't, Rose was sure she would have fun. And her first plane ride would be exciting.

They arrived at the airport and parked the car. Two men who worked at the airport took their bags. The bags would be loaded on the plane. Rose and her parents walked quickly and made it to the plane just in time.

Rose looked all around the plane. Everyone else was already in their seats. A tall lady with a blue dress walked the Lopez family to their seats. Rose sat between her mother and father.

"This is so exciting," Rose said with a smile.

During the flight to Mexico, Rose read some books and then took a nap. When Rose woke up the plane had already landed. She leaned over and looked out the window. She saw people wearing shorts.

"No one is wearing a jacket," Rose said with a puzzled look on her face. "It's February. Why isn't anyone wearing a jacket in this cold weather?"

"Because it's not cold," her father explained.

Rose still did not understand. As she stepped off the plane she could not believe how hot it was. She took off her jacket. Rose wished that she had worn a pair of shorts.

"I guess I won't need the scarf and gloves that I packed," Rose declared.

When Rose and her parents arrived at her cousins' house, everyone was so happy to see each other. Maria and Miguel took Rose to see the pool. When they came back inside the house Aunt Tula made some lemonade.

"It feels like summer," Rose said.

Uncle Hector could tell that Rose was **confused**. He took a globe from a shelf in the living room. He pointed to Mexico on the globe. He explained that Mexico was closer to the equator than Chicago. He also explained the sun's rays shone more directly on Mexico than on Chicago. Rose finally understood why it was so hot even though it was February.

Rose thought for a moment, and then shouted, "What are we waiting for. Let's go swimming!

1 **Which of the following did Rose pack for her trip?**

Ⓐ an umbrella

Ⓑ a scarf

Ⓒ a dress

Ⓓ a hat

2 **This story is mostly about**

Ⓐ a girl who wants to build a snowman

Ⓑ a girl who likes to play in the snow

Ⓒ a family going to Mexico for a vacation

Ⓓ a family flying on an airplane

3 **What happened after Rose arrived at her cousins' house?**

Ⓐ Aunt Tula made some lemonade.

Ⓑ Rose took a nap.

Ⓒ Mr. Lopez drove Rose to the pool.

Ⓓ Rose took a sweater from her closet.

4 **Read the sentence below from the story.**

"Uncle Hector could tell that Rose was *confused*."

In this sentence, the word *confused* means

Ⓐ not very happy

Ⓑ not very friendly

Ⓒ not able to do something

Ⓓ not able to understand

5 **At the beginning of the story, where is Rose?**

Ⓐ in her bedroom

Ⓑ in the kitchen

Ⓒ at the airport

Ⓓ at her cousins' house

6 **What causes Rose to wish she had worn a pair of shorts?**

_____

_____

_____

_____

_____

_____

_____

7 **How is Mexico different from Chicago?**

Ⓐ It snows more in Mexico than it does in Chicago.

Ⓑ It is colder in Mexico than it is in Chicago.

Ⓒ It is warmer in Mexico than it is in Chicago.

Ⓓ It rains more in Mexico than it does in Chicago.

A
S
S
E
S
S
M
E
N
T
S

8 **Which of the following things that Rose says is an example of a fact?**

Ⓐ "This vacation is going to be so much fun."

Ⓑ "This is so exciting."

Ⓒ "No one is wearing a jacket."

Ⓓ "It feels like summer."

9 **Which of the following will Rose most likely do while she is in Mexico?**

Ⓐ go swimming

Ⓑ build a snowman

Ⓒ wear her scarf

Ⓓ buy a sweater

10 **From reading this story, you can tell**

Ⓐ Rose has been to Mexico before

Ⓑ Rose has never been to Mexico before

Ⓒ Rose likes Mexico better than Chicago

Ⓓ Rose likes summer better than winter

11 **Why does Rose say that "It feels like summer"? Use details from the story to explain your answer.**

_____

_____

_____

_____

_____

_____

_____

_____

_____

_____

_____

_____

12 A person who reads this story could learn

Ⓐ how to build a snowman

Ⓑ how to plan a vacation

Ⓒ why it snows during the winter

Ⓓ why Mexico is warmer than Chicago

13 This story is an example of

Ⓐ a story

Ⓑ a legend

Ⓒ a poem

Ⓓ a play

14 Which of the following items should Rose pack the next time she goes to Mexico?

Ⓐ boots

Ⓑ mittens

Ⓒ sunglasses

Ⓓ ice skates

Passage 2 | **Directions:** Read the passage below and answer the questions that follow.

CHANGING SEASONS

Why is it warmer during the summer and colder during the winter? Some people think it is warmer during the summer because Earth is closer to the sun. They also think it is colder in the winter because Earth is further from the sun. However, this is not true. It is the way Earth is tilted that makes the seasons change. As Earth moves around the sun, the angle at which it is tilted changes. It is summer where you live when that part of Earth is tilted towards the sun. It is winter where you live when that part of Earth is tilted away from the sun. This is what causes the change of seasons to *occur*.

Not every place on Earth has each season at the same time of year. An imaginary line across the center of Earth divides it into two equal halves. This imaginary line is called the equator. The northern half of Earth is above this line. The southern half of Earth is below this line. When the North Pole is tilted toward the sun, it is summer in the northern half of Earth. But in the southern half of Earth, it is winter! The southern half of Earth has its summer season when the South Pole is tilted towards the sun. At that time, it is winter in the northern half of Earth.

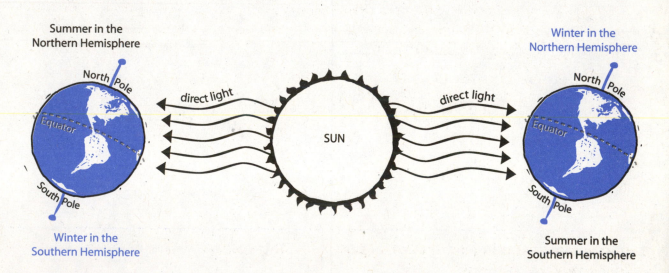

On the northern half of Earth, summer begins when the North Pole is at its greatest tilt toward the sun. This may occur on June 20, 21, or 22. On the first day of summer, the sun appears to be very high in the sky. There are more hours of sunlight in a day during the summer. In most places it is warmer in the summer than any other time of year.

Autumn is the season that follows summer. It begins on September 22 or 23. The North Pole begins to tilt away from the sun during autumn. In many places it will become cooler. There are fewer hours of daylight than in the summer.

On the northern half of Earth, winter begins when the North Pole is at its greatest tilt away from the sun. This occurs on December 21 or 22. On the first day of winter, the sun appears to be very low in the sky. There are fewer minutes of daylight on the first day of winter than on any other day. In most places it is colder in the winter than at any other time of year.

Spring is the season that follows winter. In the northern half of Earth, it begins on March 19, 20, or 21. That is when the North Pole begins to tilt towards the sun. In many places it will become warmer. There are more hours of daylight during spring than in the winter. Then as the summer season gets closer, there will be more daylight each day.

Seasons are not the only things that cause weather to change. Different parts of Earth get different amounts of sunshine. Near the equator the sunlight shines more directly on Earth. This causes that area to be hot most of the year. At the North and South Poles there is no direct sunlight, so it is very cold most of the year. Air movement also causes changes in weather. Warm air and cold air can be pushed around by wind. And places that are near the ocean are usually cooler than places far from the ocean.

Many things cause the weather to change. But how Earth is tilted towards the sun has the greatest effect. It is what causes the four seasons. Learning what causes the seasons to change is very interesting. And now you know the real story!

1 **During which season does the sun appear to be very low in the sky?**

   Ⓐ winter

   Ⓑ spring

   Ⓒ summer

   Ⓓ autumn

2 **This passage is mostly about**

   Ⓐ how many seasons there are

   Ⓑ when summer begins

   Ⓒ why there are seasons

   Ⓓ what the coldest season is

3   **What happens between the first day of spring and the first day of summer?**

   Ⓐ There are very few hours of sunlight.

   Ⓑ The amount of sunlight each day is the same.

   Ⓒ The sunlight is not as warm.

   Ⓓ There is more sunlight each day.

4   **Read the sentence below from the passage.**

   "This is what causes the change of seasons to *occur*."

   What does the word occur mean as it is used in this sentence?

   Ⓐ to appear

   Ⓑ to happen

   Ⓒ to change

   Ⓓ to enter

5   **What part of Earth is hot most of the year?**

   Ⓐ near the North Pole

   Ⓑ near the South Pole

   Ⓒ near the ocean

   Ⓓ near the equator

6   **It is winter on the northern half of Earth when**

   Ⓐ the North Pole is tilted towards the sun

   Ⓑ the South Pole is tilted towards the sun

   Ⓒ Earth is not tilted at all

   Ⓓ Earth is furthest from the sun

7   **How is the North Pole different from the South Pole?**

   Ⓐ When it is summer at the North Pole it is winter at the South Pole.

   Ⓑ When it is cold at the South Pole it is hot at the North Pole.

   Ⓒ The North Pole always has more hours of daylight than the South Pole.

   Ⓓ The South Pole is much closer to the equator than the North Pole.

8   **Which of the following is an example of an opinion?**

   Ⓐ "On the first day of summer, the sun appears to be very high in the sky."

   Ⓑ "Warm air and cold air can be pushed around by wind."

   Ⓒ "Places that are near the ocean are usually cooler than places far from the ocean."

   Ⓓ "Learning what causes the seasons to change is very interesting."

9 If Earth did NOT tilt towards the sun would there be any seasons? Explain your answer.

_____

_____

_____

_____

_____

_____

10 Why is it warmer during the summer than in the winter?

(A) There is more direct sunlight during the summer.

(B) Earth is always further from the sun during the summer.

(C) The sun is lower in the sky during the summer.

(D) There are more hours of sunlight during the summer

11 Why do seasons occur at different times of the year above the equator and below the equator? Use the drawing in the passage to help answer this question.

_____

_____

_____

_____

_____

_____

_____

_____

_____

_____

A
S
S
E
S
S
M
E
N
T
S

12 Why was this passage written?

Ⓐ to tell a story

Ⓑ to argue an opinion

Ⓒ to compare ideas

Ⓓ to give information

13 Where would you find the most information about the four seasons?

Ⓐ in a book of poetry

Ⓑ in a geography book

Ⓒ in a science textbook

Ⓓ in a newspaper

14 Which activity would a person most likely do during the summer?

Ⓐ go skiing

Ⓑ go swimming outside

Ⓒ build a snowman

Ⓓ rake leaves